Longs Peak Tales
by Glenn Randall

1981

WITHDRAWN
www.loneconelibrary.org

Copyright 1981
by Glenn Randall
All rights reserved
Library of Congress Catalogue
Card number 81-50071
ISBN 0-937050-20-2
Made in U.S.A.

Typesetting and layout by
Prepress Advertising
Denver, Colorado

Preface

Longs Peak is the monarch of the northern Colorado Rockies. It rises 14,256 feet in the heart of Rocky Mountain National Park, 40 miles northwest of Denver. For as far back as history records, human passions and human adventures have swirled around its summit like the wind. The ten stories in this book draw on that history. Though some of the dialogue has been invented in those tales whose characters can no longer tell their stories themselves, all of the tales remain true to the spirit of the facts.

Table of Contents

I	Old Man Gun
II	Lamb's Slide
III	An Englishwoman and a Desperado
IV	Wind
V	Blind on the Continental Divide
VI	Death on the East Face
VII	The Lure of the Diamond
VIII	Out of the Rocking Chair
IX	Alone on "The Casual Route"
X	A Last Adventure

Dedication

This book is dedicated to those adventurous people, living and dead, who gave Longs Peak its fascinating history. To them I express my deepest thanks.

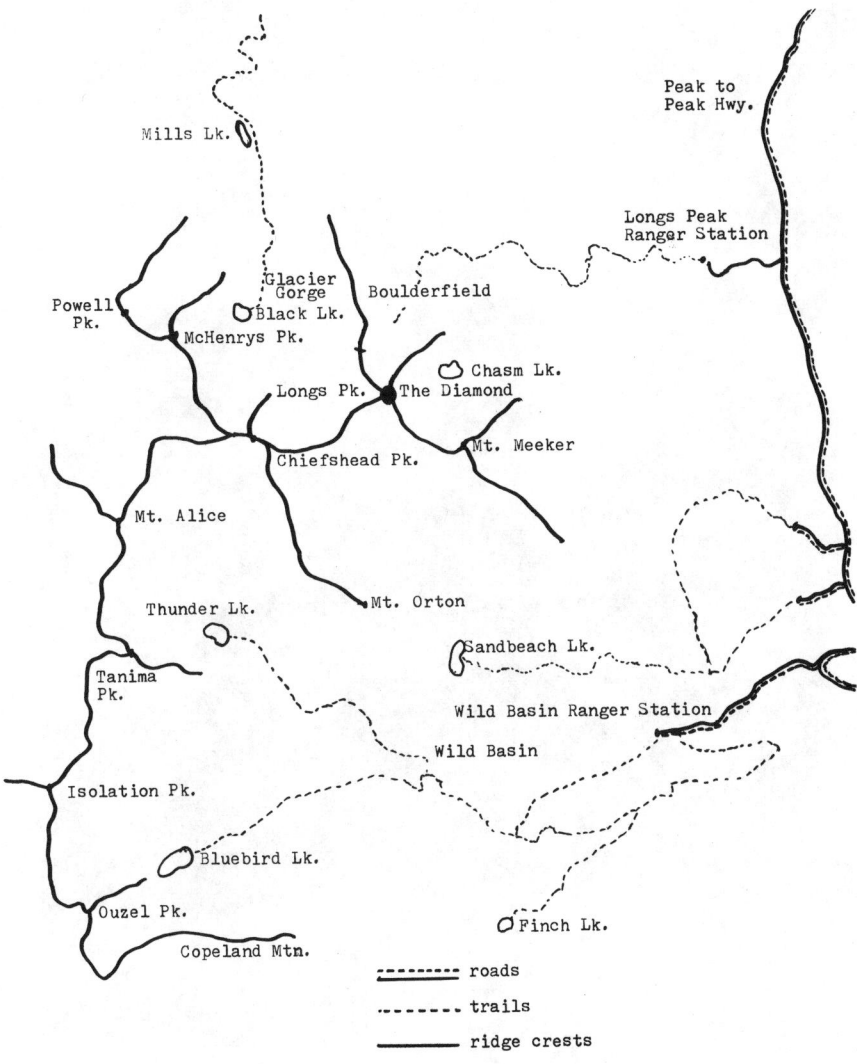

Mills Lk.

Peak to
Peak Hwy.

Longs Peak
Ranger Station

Glacier
Gorge   Boulderfield

Powell
Pk.   Black Lk.
          McHenrys Pk.

          Chasm Lk.
Longs Pk. The Diamond

          Chiefshead Pk.   Mt. Meeker

Mt. Alice

Thunder Lk.   Mt. Orton

                Sandbeach Lk.
Tanima
Pk.   Wild Basin Ranger Station

Isolation Pk.   Wild Basin

          Bluebird Lk.

Ouzel Pk.   Finch Lk.
     Copeland Mtn.

- - - - - - - roads
- - - - - - . trails
_____ ridge crests

In 1858 Old Man Gun's son, Gun Griswold (center), climbed Longs Peak from Wild Basin in search of his father's eagle trap. Fifty-five years later, Gun Griswold told Oliver Toll of his climb and unsuccessful search for the trap.

Photo courtesy the Colorado Historical Society.

OLD MAN GUN

The danger had passed; but the fear haunted them still, the fear felt by men who have been attacked from behind without warning. In silence the five Arapaho warriors rode into camp. Five ponies with empty saddles trailed behind. They dismounted at the tipi of Yellow Horse, an elder of the tribe, and went inside. One of them limped; another's arm hung useless. Other warriors from the small camp of 10 tipis came in one by one and seated themselves in the circle. By tradition, Old Man Gun should have told what had happened; but Two Elk's voice broke the silence first.

"We went out 10 strong to raid upon the Utes camped two days to the northwest. You have seen how many came back — five! You, Gun, you were the leader — the dead lie on your shoulders." He paused, breathing hard.

"First some miserable Ute scout discovered us. Then the Utes retreated to that hilltop they have fortified with stones and timber. We had gone to steal horses, but Gun wanted to count coup and led a direct attack. It failed. That night some Ute must have slipped away from the fort. He stole one of *our* horses and escaped to the main Ute camp. And when we attacked again at dawn you ordered no one to guard our rear. Then 20 Utes attacked from behind. Now five brave warriors are dead. My son is dead — and yours."

Old Man Gun listened without words, every muscle in his aging face drawn bow-string taut. The ancient wound where the first joint of his little finger was missing ached and throbbed. All eyes were upon him. Gun knew Two Elk spoke truly. For 30 years, since he was just a Kit Fox of 17, Gun had fought Utes, Pawnees and Osage. Always he had fought with honor, and when he recited his coups after a raid the counting took much time. Now this: after 30 years, what was happening?

"We will take revenge," he said. "I myself will lead."

"Oh, you will lead, will you?" Two Elk cut in. "And where will you find the warriors to follow you?"

"I will take revenge!" Gun cried. "Who will follow me?" In vain his eyes summoned each warrior in turn. As well conjure ashes to burn, thought Gun. How different from years past!

Two Elk spoke again. "A revenge raid can only fail. The Utes would come down on us like the north wind. We are too weak now, scattered in our winter camps. The Dog Society will forbid you to take revenge." No warrior seated in the tipi disagreed. "When we rejoin our brothers for the summer buffalo hunt, then, perhaps, we will consider raids and revenge."

Gun strode outside as the meeting broke up and stomped through the mud and slush to his tent. The melting of the foothill snows heralded the approaching end of the winter camp, but Gun ached for vengeance now. Those icy, accusing eyes, the fathers and brothers of those who had died — he could not endure them for another moon.

Slowly the light faded inside Gun's tipi. The evening shadows of the peak white men called Longs crept over the camp. Gun brooded until, exhausted, he fell into a fitful sleep. His body relaxed; but his mind churned on. He dreamed of his youth, when he had first set out on a vision quest. In his dream he relived his search. Alone, naked but for breechcloth and moccasins, he wandered away from camp. For four days he fasted and thirsted. No vision came. At sunset, on the final day that tradition would allow for such a quest, he again faced west and stared into the sun without blinking. The sun's rim touched the horizon. He raised his hands and cried out, "Hear me!" His voice echoed among the rocks and died away. The silence struck him like a fist. He snatched his knife from his belt, stooped over a rock and slashed downward. A strangled moan twisted his lips. He held the bloody, severed finger joint aloft and cried, "Father's clansman, you see me. I am pitiable. This is a part of my body. I give it to you. Eat it! And give me your strength."

He had fainted from the pain. Half-conscious, in his dream, he seemed to see a spirit come to him from the west in the form of a warrior dressed in white buckskin with an eagle feather headdress reaching to his ankles.

"I have heard you," the spirit said. "I will give you strength in battle and skillful aim in the hunt. You will live a long and honored life. Build an eagle trap in a high and lonely place. Wait there four days, no more. Within four days I will send an eagle. The eagle will not truly die. Its spirit will return to me. You will wear the feathers as a sign my power is with you." As the spirit faded, it seemed to Gun's sun-dazzled eyes that the warrior became an eagle with white head and tail and a great, hooked yellow beak.

Gun's sleep evaporated with the dream. He threw back his buffalo robe and sat up. The time had come to renew his pact with his Elder Brother. He would again build an eagle trap, as he had done so many years before. Only the highest peak he knew of, the one that cast its evening shadows across the camp, would do. On its summit — if he could reach it — he would dig a pit and wait inside, with tallow for bait and a stuffed coyote to make the bait look natural. If an eagle came, and he could kill without weapons, he would know his Elder Brother had not deserted him. Then, with eagle down as a token of Elder Brother's power, he would take revenge. Alone, he would go to the Ute camp. Alone, he would count many coups, steal many horses and vanish.

Gun stepped from the tent. The stars told him the night was but half gone. He returned inside and began to stuff by feel the things he would need into two rawhide pouches. Then he caught and saddled his favorite war pony and rode quietly into the forest.

By first light the lowland ponderosa had given way to lodgepole pine. Gun rode on, deeper and deeper into country he had never seen before. The snow already stood three handspans deep on his pony's shanks. Behind him his tracks, tinted pink by the rising sun, stood out like the tracks of a buffalo. Any Utes nearby would certainly know he had passed. "Be watchful, always," he told himself, and went on.

He hobbled his pony at timberline and savored a mouthful of dried buffalo meat. While at his eagle trap he would neither eat nor drink. His grandfather had said, years before, "You must go to the eagle trap clean in spirit, humble, not proud. If anyone questions you, say only, 'Perhaps I will kill.' Never boast."

His meal finished, Gun scanned the way ahead. Deep snow lay on the lower reaches of the mountain. Above, the wind had blasted the snow away, leaving exposed boulder-strewn slopes and polished granite slabs. The wind blew there still; he could see the snow-devils whirling across the slope.

His troubles began almost immediately. Though he had brought small snowshoes of rawhide stretched across a willow frame he sank to his knees or beyond at every step. When the way grew rocky, he left the snowshoes behind, but he found he still had to cross occasional patches of snow. Here his foot plunged often into a crevice between boulders, battering his shins, only scantily protected by his deerhide leggings, and forcing him to flounder about for a secure footing. Three hours later he had gone only half a mile. He looked back at his pony waiting patiently in the snow. For a long moment he wanted simply to mount him and ride back to camp. He could tell Two Elk he had gone hunting and wait till the Arapahoes gathered for the summer buffalo hunt to seek revenge. But he thought of those damning eyes, and turned his face to the mountain again. Every ten steps he stopped to pant and search the sky: empty, lifeless, ice blue. He toiled on.

At noon he had gained half the distance between timberline and the summit. He could hop from rock to rock now, and his pace quickened.

Just below the top an icy crack splitting a steep slab brought him to a halt. A glance west told him only three hours of sunlight remained. He could not dawdle. Trusting the friction of leather on granite, he started out onto the slab. A moccasin slipped on a gritty place; then it struck clean stone and held. Minutes later he stepped onto the summit. The wind made him shiver with every gust. He began to search the stony summit plateau for a crevice he could enlarge enough to admit his body. Choosing the largest, he began to shift boulders one by one. His hands grew numb, and bled from a dozen scrapes. He piled the rocks into a hollow mound with his deepening pit in the middle. When the sun stood only a finger's width above the horizon, he straightened his back and looked on his work with a smile. Turning to the sun, he chanted a prayer of thanks. Then he began the descent.

Darkness caught him halfway down, but by then he had reached the snow and could see his tracks in the starlight. At his pony he tore into his food

3

Here on the summit of Longs Peak, Old Man Gun built his trap and waited. Photo by Glenn Randall.

pouch without pause. From another pouch he drew double handfuls of dried grass and scattered them on the snow for the pony. Then he broke pine boughs off the nearest tree, laid them thickly on the snow, rolled himself into his buffalo robe and fell asleep.

He had slept but minutes, or so it seemed, when he awoke and examined the stars. Half the night gone, and still he lay abed. He threw back the robe. The air like ice water penetrated his clothes immediately. Stilling his shivering with an effort, he took a handful of snow and washed his face and hands. Then he took paints from a rawhide pouch, mixed them with buffalo-back fat, and began to apply them to his face: white clay for the snow, blue clay for the Rocky Mountains, charcoal for the dark-bodied bald eagle he hoped to trap. He took tobacco from another pouch and filled a small, straight pipe. With stiffened fingers he struck a spark from his flint into tinder and breathed a tiny flame into the tobacco. He offered a puff of smoke to each of the four directions, chanting, "Elder Brother, hear my prayer. Make my hands swift and strong. Bring a winged one to my trap. Hear me!" Then he began to climb.

With a track already broken and the pitfalls amidst the boulders already marked by previous struggles, he gained height rapidly. Under cover of darkness, as he had planned, he slipped into the pit. He tied one end of a rawhide thong to some tallow, and led the other into the pit. Then he shifted a thin slab of granite partway over the trap's entrance and settled down to wait. The day passed like an icicle melting, drop by drop. Jagged boulders jabbed his spine, and his knees ached from hours of sitting. The sky remained empty. Just before sunset he pushed the granite slab aside and hoisted himself from the trap with his arms. His cramped legs could barely support him. The rush of blood made him reel. He swallowed hard, throat dry as though he were chewing sand. Hobbling over to the edge of the summit plateau, he faced the murky outline of the sun, half-hidden behind a deepening overcast. Slowly he raised his hands. Again he chanted, but his words came out as a croak and he did not know whether Elder Brother heard. He offered tobacco and turned toward camp.

He tripped often as he struggled downward under starless skies. One hundred yards from camp he caught sight of his pony's white saddle-blanket. Numb with fatigue, he didn't heed the warning signal until it was almost too late. Then he froze. No welcoming neigh had rung out to greet him. What was scaring the pony into silence? Mountain lion? Bear?

The vicious swish of an arrow in flight answered all questions. Utes! He turned and fled. A second arrow ripped through the air as he swerved from his beaten track and plunged into the woods. The darkness under the trees made him nearly invisible. On he fled, his lungs filled to bursting with every breath. He could no longer hear his pursuers. He slowed his pace and listened. They must have lost his trail. Then he thought of another, more frightening possibility. He stopped, every muscle tensed. Only his rasping breath broke the silence. What if they simply waited till morning and followed his tracks? He could not outrun them forever. He could not hide. A crawling babe could track him down. He could stand and fight. At least he would die honorably. Then a plan began to form in his mind, so simple — and so dangerous. Everything hinged on his enemies' cunning. Had they lost his trail? Or had they already outwitted him and resolved to wait till morning to track him down? He could only go find out.

He began retracing his steps, planting each foot in an already-made track. As he neared his camp he slowed. Every third step he paused to listen. Then, to his right, not more than a stone's throw away, he heard a thud and a muffled curse. He laughed soundlessly. Some hapless Ute pony had stumbled over a downed tree in the dark and sent its rider sprawling. The Utes had indeed lost his trail. They could only pursue him now in the morning, and by then he would be long gone.

At camp he hushed his pony with a whisper, turned him loose and headed him toward home. Taking only one buffalo robe with him, he again began to climb. In the morning the Utes would either follow his trail of the night before or hurry after his pony, thinking him with it. Both trails would dead end. When they realized where he had actually gone, they would be unlikely to pursue him, for above timberline he could see them coming from a great distance. With the night almost gone, he stamped out a platform in the snow far above the nearest trees, curled up in his blanket and fell asleep.

He awoke with the feeling that his blanket had somehow grown heavy in the night. He tried to shove it back and was rewarded with a fistful of snow down his sleeve. He pushed the blanket aside more strongly and sat up, blinking in the sunlight of mid-morning and cursing. A chill wind gusted across the snow, picking up spindrift in swirling eddies. During the night the spindrift had buried him completely, shutting out the light of the sun. Now the day's eagle hunt was spoiled, for the eagles would surely see him as he approached the trap. Two days wasted and only two to go!

All day he sat hugging his knees and rocking back and forth to keep warm, watching for Utes. At sunset he resumed his climb, determined to spend the night in the trap. Hours before first light he crawled into the pit and partially covered the opening with the slab. For a few hours he managed a restless sleep. At sunrise he resumed his vigil.

As if weighted by stones the sun journeyed across the sky. Sheltered from the wind by the pit and warmed by his blanket, Gun's eyelids drooped. Gradually his hand grew limp on the thong that led to the bait. His eyes closed.

He awoke with a start as the thong ripped through his hand. Too late his fingers clamped shut. He heard a thin squawk and caught a glimpse of feathers, dark and flashing white, as a bald eagle with a wingspan of fully seven feet launched itself into the sky with the tallow in its beak. He tossed aside the slab, and watched, aching and stiff from sleeping too long on hard stone, as the eagle swept away from the mountain. It climbed in ever-widening circles, then headed west till Gun lost sight of it in the sun. His shoulders sagged, and his hands opened and closed helplessly. "Gone," he whispered. "Gone."

No other eagles came by nightfall. A thin veil of clouds again began to darken the western sky, blotting out the stars one by one. Gun began to worry. Only one day was left in the hunt, and a storm would drive any eagle away for certain.

With darkness complete, Gun descended a few hundred feet to a level place sheltered from the wind. The trap was too confining and the exposed summit too cold for a good camp. Hunkered down in his blanket, he gnawed a mouthful of dried meat. His stomach demanded more, but he knew he must save his last piece for bait. Eyes closed, holding in both hands a final remnant of tobacco, he chanted the song Elder Brother had taught him in his first vision, asking for strength and another chance. Then he drifted into a restless sleep.

Sunshine touched his camp for only a minute at dawn. Then the sun vanished as the clouds engulfed the eastern horizon. Each step demanded effort as he climbed to his trap for the last time. He placed the scrap of meat outside the trap and arranged the thong. Uncounted hours passed without the sun to mark time. The gloom deepened. A snowflake drifted out of the clouds and landed without melting on the bait.

He had almost decided to leave the trap for just a minute to stretch his knotted muscles when his ears caught the soft swish of wings. His grip tightened on the thong.

Suddenly the eagle's wings seemed to cover the sky. An instant later the eagle plunged its talons into the bait. Gun yanked the bait toward him with his left hand and seized the eagle's feet with his right. The eagle lashed out with its beak and Gun's right hand spouted blood. He almost lost his hold. Then his left hand let go of the rawhide and seized the eagle's feet. Heaving the slab aside with his shoulders, he dragged the eagle toward him. The wings buffeted his head. The yellow beak flashed out again and laid his scalp open from hairline to eyebrow. Nearly blind from the blood, Gun lunged from the trap and tried to crush the eagle beneath his weight. His hands sought the neck, groping. Another slashing blow told him where the head was, and his hands closed, strongly, twisting, till the thrashing body beneath him grew still.

Gun wiped the blood from his eyes and stood up. The clouds swept low over the summit. Sleet borne horizontally by the wind stung Gun's face and encrusted his hair. He held the eagle aloft, blood streaming down his arms. His cry came from the pit of his stomach: "With your help, Elder Brother, I will again be a warrior! I will take revenge!"

The Reverend Elkanah J. Lamb.
Photo courtesy the Colorado Historical Society.

HOW LAMB'S SLIDE GOT ITS NAME

A simple shortcut: that's all the Reverend Elkanah J. Lamb had in mind. He stood on the summit of Longs Peak and peered down the east side. It certainly *looked* easy — at least as far as he could see, which wasn't far. He had come up the long, bothersome Keyhole route. Thought it started boldly on the east, it ended up creeping three-quarters of the way around the mountain before striking for the top. Now Elkanah wanted to scamper directly down the east side to that alluring lake 2,000 feet below. From there, he could hike easily to his camp at timberline.

On the way up he had seen the top of his proposed shortcut from the Boulderfield, a vast plain of granite at 12,800 feet. Mt. Lady Washington had hid the bottom half behind outflung ridges. Even Elkanah could tell that the right side of the face would have thwarted a mountain goat, much less a 39-year-old itinerant preacher from Nebraska. But he thought he had spied an easier way, down ledges to the left of the diamond-shaped precipice. No one had ever climbed up that way, of course; Griffith Evans, the hotelkeeper in Estes Park, had told him the mountain had only been climbed for the first time three years before. But going down had to be easier than going up; after all, he'd have gravity on his side. As for the part he couldn't see, he'd just deal with that when he got there. "God is obliged to answer earnest prayers," he had told himself.

Elkanah did not pretend to be a mountaineer. He had been to Colorado once before, when the '59ers shouted "Gold!" to an eager nation, but that had been 11 years ago. After the summer of mining he had returned to his Nebraska farm, pockets empty but eyes filled to bursting with God's mountains. For 11 years, plagued by drought and civil war, he longed for them. In the spring of 1871 he left his wife and children in Nebraska and returned to Colorado as a missionary for the United Brethren.

From May until August he labored building Loveland's first United Brethren church. Every morning he watched the sun redden Longs' stony crown while sipping his first cup of coffee. Then the day came when he pounded the last nail home with three swift, sure blows. The next morning he set off on his long-planned trip to Estes Park. Two fellow preachers rode beside him. Brother Ross, a stingy, cadaverous man, rode a swaybacked beast that looked half starved. Brother Charlton's mare was swaybacked, too, but only when she was carrying Charlton's jovial weight. A boy drove Elkanah's wagon, and six other stout believers, including Ross' wife Sarah, shared the wagon bed with an ample supply of coffee beans.

For two days they journeyed across the plains, stopping early each day to preach at little towns. Then they entered the mountains at the canyon of the St. Vrain River. On the fourth day, in the cool evening twilight, they arrived in Estes Park and rented a cabin at Griffith Evans' rude hotel. After supper they hitched their chairs closer to the fire in Evans' parlor.

"Ready to try for the Peak tomorrow, Brother Ross?" Elkanah asked.

Another of Evans' guests cut off Ross' reply.

"My, are you going to climb Longs Peak? May I go too?" Without waiting for an answer she added, "My name is Genevieve." She gave a little curtsy.

Ross had just started to open his mouth again when a rather portly matron announced, "My name is Eleanor May Burkhardt, and I've been trying to find a guide to Longs Peak all week. My daughter Louisa would like to go too, wouldn't you, dear."

Ross seized the momentary silence. "Yes, Elkanah, I'm ready to try for the Peak." He paused. "And I think Sarah is interested as well."

Elkanah watched with a mixture of amusement and outrage as Genevieve and Eleanor May bustled about gathering their duffel into piles.

"This absolutely *must* go," Genevieve exclaimed, brandishing a frying pan the breadth of a barrel top. "I just *can't* cook without it!" Elkanah grimaced and privately reckoned that Genevieve's horse, if not Genevieve herself, would poop out well before timberline.

Elkanah rose before the cock crowed the next morning and began corralling the horses. They planned to camp the first night at timberline, eight miles distant. One by one the other "mountaineers" emerged from their cabins, yawning, and made a beeline for the kitchen, where Evans was flipping flapjacks like a juggler in a circus. Elkanah finished the packing alone then fed his six-foot frame with two stacks of buckwheat pancakes, a pint of maple syrup and a quart of coffee. "Longs Peak or bust!" Genevieve shrilled. With a general cheer, the cavalcade lumbered off towards Longs, Elkanah leading the way.

Sunset found them unloading the horses at timberline.

"Where's that other parcel of blankets, Elkanah?" Ross asked.

"I thought you loaded them up after breakfast."

"Not I," Ross replied. He looked from Elkanah to Carlton and back again. "Somebody's going to be sleeping mighty close to the fire tonight."

"We can't ask the ladies to go without blankets," Charlton said.

Elkanah looked disgusted. "All right, I'll stay up and keep the fire going. Will you join me, Charlton?"

"I guess I'll have to."

At sunset the temperature dropped into the 30s. Elkanah and Charlton built the cooking coals into a bonfire. The rest rolled themselves into blankets. Elkanah drew his overcoat tighter around him and watched the stars slip behind the outline of Granite Pass. Toward dawn he lay down, hoping the fire would last long enough to give him a little sleep. His thoughts drifted back to Nebraska. "Do you think they wonder about the wandering Lamb?" he whispered to Charlton, but Charlton was fast asleep.

At breakfast Elkanah took one sip of Ross' coffee and roared, "How many times do I have to tell you, Ross! If you can't float a horseshoe on the brew, throw in more coffee beans!"

Elkanah ladled out another bowlful of oatmeal, asking a rather queasy-looking Genevieve, "Aren't you hungry this morning? Mountain air really gives me an appetite!"

Genevieve turned green as Elkanah scraped a slab of cold bacon grease out of the previous night's frying pan and stirred it vigorously into steaming glop.

"I'll just wait for you here," she said.

Charlton set down his untouched bowl. "I'll keep you company."

Elkanah ran his spoon around the edge of the now-empty pot. "Well, that leaves five of us," he said. "Let's get going."

Elkanah quickly outdistanced the others. At the Boulderfield he waited. Perched on a rock like a great black crow, knees pulled inside his ankle-length coat, he examined the east face. Already, at noon, the sun had abandoned the wall. A thunderstorm two days before had dropped snow that still clung to slopes just below the summit. In places, melting snow had run down over the edge of the precipice and refrozen into ice-curtains fanged like a dragon's maw.

"That's one lion's den this Daniel is going to stay out of," Elkanah said. "But I wonder if you could get down off to the left . . ." His eyes traced the maze and encountered one dead end after another. Before he discovered the solution — if one existed — Sarah interrupted his reverie.

"I can't go another step." She collapsed onto a boulder. "Stay with me, won't you dear?" Her husband, breathing hard, did not reply.

Eleanor May wheezed up next and plopped her quivering bulk down nearby. "Oh dear," she said, looking at the way ahead.

Louisa dragged in last. "I wish I was back in Estes," she snapped and stuck out her tongue at her mother. For once, Eleanor May was speechless.

Elkanah offered everyone biscuits from his pack. Not even Ross took a nibble. Elkanah shrugged and munched on them by himself. He tossed the crumbs to a chattering marmot.

"Who's coming with me to the top?" he asked.

No one looked up.

"We've got to climb higher than this if we want to get to heaven," he said. No one laughed.

"All right, I'll go by myself. I'll meet you at camp." He tramped away, singing a hymn.

The east face of Longs Peak dominates Chasm Lake at sunrise. Elkanah descended from the summit down slopes just beneath the prominent notch on the left-hand skyline, then traversed left above the steep, water-streaked wall and back down a gully to the right to Mills Glacier, the large snowfield at the base of the east face.   Photo by Glenn Randall.

"Possessed of God is right," Ross muttered. "Just like his name says."

In a few minutes Elkanah reached the Keyhole, an almost circular notch in Longs north ridge. His eyes drank in the mountains rising in wave after wave out to the horizon. Then he traversed slabs and narrow sandy ledges to the Trough, a gully leading to the west ridge.

"Why, I'm almost there," he cried and bounded up the gully as if it were a Nebraska cornfield.

Within 30 paces every breath was racking his lungs. "Got to slow down," he gasped. He toiled upward for several minutes, eyes on his footing, then looked up. The top of the gully seemed as distant as ever. He set off again. Puffing hard a few minutes later, he checked his progress. The ridge crest seemed to have receded in front of him. He settled down now to the grind.

An hour later than he had expected, he reached the west ridge. When his heartbeat returned to normal, he edged across a skinny ledge that Evans had called the Narrows.

"It's as steep as a church steeple!" he exclaimed, eyeing the final slabs below the summit. "Just pretend you're building the church roof in Loveland," he told himself, and scrambled upward to the top.

"What almighty power, to build such mountains!" he whispered. Everywhere within a 180-degree arc, peaks punctured the horizon. The last of winter's snowfields gleamed under the parching August sun. Their waters seeped unseen down through boulders and alpine meadows, then burst forth in waterfalls visible even miles away. To the west, ranks of thunderheads, black as soot beneath and fluffy as popcorn above, interrupted Elkanah's delight. Dark streamers of rain, not yet reaching the ground, hung beneath a few of the clouds. "Get on over to Nebraska where you belong," he told the thunderheads.

Elkanah turned and hopped from rock to rock across the boulder-strewn summit, heading for the eastern edge. "I can almost see home!" he exclaimed. "Somewhere, right out there . . ."

For an hour he feasted on the view. Then a shadow swept over the peak as the sun vanished behind the approaching thunderheads. Elkanah glanced over his shoulder.

"I'll just go down the east face," he decided. "It'll be faster. I never did like the smell of wet lamb skin."

At first, the mountainside sloped gently, but a 50-foot cliff soon brought him to a halt. He began exploring the clifftop, looking for a place he could descend. Closer and closer he came to the edge of the diamond-shaped precipice itself, until it seemed that his little cliff would simply merge with the greater one and leave him stymied. The shelf between the two had narrowed to a few feet when Elkanah found a place where the smaller cliff was broken into a giant's staircase, each step five feet tall. He started sliding down over the steps on the seat of his pants. At the third an ominous rip told him the already-frayed cloth had finally parted. As he landed, his feet skidded out from under him and dislodged a stone. It bounced once and vanished into the void. Elkanah held his breath, listening, but he never heard it strike again.

The last step was at least twice as tall as the rest. Elkanah searched vainly for a way around. The grassy ledge at the bottom had a noticeable tilt toward Chasm Lake, 2,000 feet below. Elkanah faced in to the rock and let himself down over the edge. Even hanging by his fingertips, his feet dangled five feet above the terrace. He dragged himself back over the edge with trembling arms. If he let himself drop, and landed and bounced — he shuddered to think. "I'd be a lost Lamb, that's for sure, unless I took a lucky bounce and landed in Chasm Lake."

He hunted again for other ways. None appeared. He could always go back over the top, of course, but he was tired and hated to waste the effort. His drying sweat made him shiver as he stood debating. A solitary raindrop splashed on his coat. Once more he studied the ledge below. "All I've got to do is fall toward the rock when I hit, not away," he thought. "Can't be that hard."

He squirmed down over the lip on his belly and lowered himself until his arms were outstretched. Chasm Lake swam across his field of view when he glanced between his feet. He tried to drag himself back up, but his arms felt paralyzed. His fingers were weakening. He glued his eyes to the ledge. Then he let go.

The grass gave way more than he expected and he started to go over backwards. He let his knees bend and crashed into the ledge, burying both hands in the matted sod. His momentum was still throwing him over backwards and his fingers clenched at the roots. A huge chunk of sod came loose in his right hand and he sprawled over on his left side. He tried to shove himself farther onto the ledge with a convulsive kick but his feet met only air. Then he sank his right hand back into the soil and stopped himself.

"Helpful gravity, indeed!" he spluttered. He brushed a little gravel off his coat and glanced back up at the wall. Then he began to examine it more carefully.

"I'm not sure I could get back up that thing," he said. "I sure hope I don't have to try."

Elkanah scrambled away from the main precipice along the widening shelf. Soon he reached a gully full of loose stones. For a thousand feet he skipped merrily down, riding one sliding stone till he lost his balance, then hopping to the next. Some rocks accelerated when he started them rolling and bounced down the gully ahead of him, echoing like distant thunder.

"The Lamb's starting a landslide," he thought gleefully. Then the gully ended at the top of another cliff.

A fifteen-minute search revealed a series of ledges. Elkanah climbed down to the lowest. Carefully he crept to the edge and peeped over. Below him was the portion of the face hidden when he had plotted his route from the Boulderfield. His eyes searched for any flaw in the sweeping granite. Then he stepped back from the edge and sagged to the ground. The wall below was utterly unclimbable.

"It's too late to go back now. And besides, I'd never get back up that cliff." He sat gazing at his hands as the minutes slipped away. A raindrop struck the back of his hand. Only a few patches of blue still showed in the ashen sky. To the left, as he faced out, the cliff below the ledge only grew taller. But maybe to the right he could find a way. He could see a long snow-filled gully leading up to nearly his height far to the right. A gray gleam from the surface told him part of the snow was actually ice. Still, if the ledge led that far, he might have a chance.

Almost immediately he encountered a wagon-sized granite block astride all but six inches of the ledge. Elkanah reached blindly around the corner of the block. His groping fingers found a tiny flake. He tried to reach farther, but the block started forcing him over backwards. His feet grated on the gravel. His fingers tiptoed another inch — and latched on to a flake as good as a jug handle. He stepped around the corner onto a broad ledge. The way ahead looked easy clear to the gully. Elkanah whooped.

At the gully Elkanah kicked his smooth-soled leather boot into the snow. The first blow barely scuffed the surface. After five minutes of vigorous kicking, however, he fashioned a foothold two inches wide. He took a stone and threw it into the center of the gully. The spraying crystals told him the snow was softer there. If he could only reach the center of the gully he could kick steps down it to the level boulders surrounding Chasm Lake, now only 1,000 feet below.

A few rocks protruded from the snow in the first 20 feet of the gully width, but they were too far apart to be used as stepping stones. Elkanah teetered up onto his first foothold with his left foot and immediately realized that he would need that foot for kicking the next step. He stepped off the ice then stood up on the foothold with his right foot. He kicked the next foothold and stepped up with his left foot. Balanced precariously, he wondered how on earth to get his left foot free to kick the next step.

With his fingernails he scratched two minute depressions into the ice. Then he hopped up into the air, pulled his left boot tip from the hold and landed with his right toe snuggled securely onto the tiny shelf. He smiled and kicked another hold — a little smaller this time, for his calves were beginning to ache. Again he switched feet with a graceful hop. His fourth step was smaller still, and try as he might, it still seemed to slope. He hesitated a minute before trying to switch feet. Then he leaped into the air.

His right toe slipped into the hold, banged into the bottom and bounced right back out. His fingernails clawed at the useless handholds. In an instant all control vanished as he sped down the slope. His overcoat inverted itself and started flapping around his ears. He bounced off a boulder protruding from the ice then lunged for another and missed. The sudden movement spun him around so that he was sliding face first. A third boulder flashed by in a blur. Then Elkanah caught sight of the last outcrop. Below it the snow stretched unbroken to the stones awaiting him far below. As he skidded by he wrapped both arms around its crown. His body pivoted violently around the boulder, and he hung on, gasping. His feeble kicks eventually fashioned a hold, and he struggled up onto the rock.

Elkanah's breathless toboggan ride had carried him to a portion of the gully with softer snow. He dug several handfuls of the icy powder out of the gaping hole in the seat of his pants, but the rest escaped and gathered around his knees, melting slowly. This time Elkanah kicked broad steps side by side and avoided any kangaroo hops. After 20 feet the snow softened more. Elkanah started straight down, kicking and kicking until he felt his toes would emerge from his heels. Unnoticed, the clouds crept lower. A clammy mist enveloped him. At last he stood on level snow at the foot of the gully. Fat raindrops began pelting his uncovered head, and he laughed.

An hour's trotting over the boulders took him back to camp. Ross came out to scold him.

"Where have you been?" he demanded. "We've been worried sick!"

"Fire up some coffee, brother! I've been climbing mountains and starting landslides, and I just about went on a Lamb's slide myself!"

Isabella Bird just before her marriage to Dr. John Bishop, March 1881. Photo courtesy the Colorado Historical Society.

AN ENGLISHWOMAN AND A DESPERADO

"Excuse me, gentlemen," the proprietor of Longmont's St. Vrain Hotel said to the young lawyers who had just arrived. "There is an Englishwoman here named Isabella Bird. She is traveling for her health. She would like to ride with you to Estes Park tomorrow. Would you mind?"

Platt Rogers, 23, fresh out of Columbia Law School and eager to roam unfettered, looked at his companion and frowned.

"What do you think, Downer? She'll slow us down."

"We can't very well refuse. Perhaps she'll be young and beautiful."

At 8:30 the next morning Isabella appeared in the hotel courtyard, dressed in a travel-worn fitted jacket, a full length skirt cinched tight above her ample hips and turkish trousers that bagged at the knees and fell in gathered frills over her boots.

"She must be over 40," Rogers whispered to Downer, "and half as wide as she is tall." Isabella ignored their sniggers and flung her 4-foot, 11½-inch frame atop her horse, silently cursing the skirt that forced her to ride sidesaddle.

"Let us be off!" she cried and spurred her horse from the courtyard. The young men glanced at each other and followed.

Soon they were cantering across the plains toward St. Vrain Canyon. A mile outside of town, Isabella dismounted, stripped off her skirt and remounted astride. "It's so much easier on my back," she explained. "I had a tumor removed from my spine when I was 16. My back has pained me ever since."

Isabella easily kept up with Rogers and Downer. She had been on horseback ever since her legs could reach the shortened stirrups. Eight hours of hard riding took them across 15 miles of prairie, up the rock-walled St. Vrain Canyon, then over pass after pass. Only the prattle of her town-bred companions marred Isabella's delight. She longed to speak to someone who loved the mountains as she did. Soon, she hoped, she would have the opportunity. Just ahead lay the cabin of Rocky Mountain Jim Nugent. Isabella had heard tales of him from friends in England who had visited Estes the year before. "He's a gentleman when sober but a ruffian when drunk, which is often," they said.

Minutes later Jim's black homestead came into view. Isabella reined in abruptly. The cabin looked uninhabitable. Smoke seeped from both windows and chimney. Lynx and beaver pelts lay drying on the mud-covered roof, and a skinned beaver carcass lay just inside the door. Deer antlers mingled with the horseshoes and offal that lay in stinking piles around the cabin. "It looks like the den of a wild animal!" Isabella said.

Before she could move on, the growls of a big collie brought Jim to the door. Isabella swiftly took in the details. He was about 45, middle height, with large, gray-blue eyes set deeply beneath bushy brows. His dense mustache complimented the tawny hair that hung in curls from beneath his battered cap. He must once have been handsome, but some accident had left half his face hideously scarred. His good profile, though, bore a striking resemblance to Shakespeare's.

Jim silenced the dog with a moccasined foot, then tipped his hat to Isabella with a flourish and said, "Good afternoon, madam. It is such a pleasure to have visitors. What can I do for you?"

"Well, ah, a drink of water would be nice," she stammered. Jim disappeared into the cabin. "A surprisingly chivalrous gentleman!" Isabella said to Rogers. "Only when he wants to be, or so I've heard," Rogers replied.

Jim reappeared with water in a dented tin can.

"My apologies for the crude utensil," he said in a musical Irish brogue. "May I ask where you are from?"

"From England," she said, "but I've been traveling around the world for the past 15 months. I just left Hawaii three weeks ago. Such marvelous flowers and birds there, and the mountains! I climbed Mauna Loa while I was there, but I must say that Longs Peak is the most glorious mountain I've seen in either hemisphere. I would so much love to climb it."

"Aye, it's a beauty," Jim said. "Splendid country around here. Full of elk, deer, beaver — and bears, too. That's how I lost my eye. I was hunting in Middle Park when my dog,Ring,scared up a grizzly sow and two cubs. She charged, and my mule shied and threw me. I put four bullets in her before she downed me, but she clawed me head to foot and broke my left arm before she died. When I came to, I was lying in a pool of blood. Bear blood, mostly. My mule got me down the trail and a sawbones patched me up almost as good as new."

"You're a brave man, Mr. Nugent," Isabella said.

"Why, thank you, Miss —?"

"Bird," Isabella said. "Isabella Bird."

"Thank you, Miss Bird. I hope you will allow me the pleasure of calling on you during your stay in Estes Park."

"It will be my pleasure," Isabella said. "We must be off, I fear, if we want to reach Mr. Evans' by sundown. Good day."

As they rode away Downer said, "Rather funny, don't you think, hearing an Irish brogue coming from a southern gentleman? At least, he boasted once in the Bucket of Blood that he was the son of a Confederate general."

"That's odd," Rogers replied, "I overheard him say once that he was a Connecticut Yankee."

"He's a most interesting man, don't you think?" Isabella said. "Such fascinating stories!"

They arrived in twilight at the rude hostel run by Griffith Evans, a cheerful, hard-drinking Welshman. After supper, as Evans and his guests sat near the fire in the lodge, Isabella asked Evans about a guide for Longs Peak.

"It's pretty late in the season," Evans replied. "Nasty storms brew up in October. I'll guide you, if the weather holds, but I have to go to Denver tomorrow for flour."

"Can anyone else guide me?" Isabella asked.

"Well, Jim might be able to," Evans said. He turned to Rogers and Downer. "Do you want to go too?"

"Most certainly," Rogers replied.

"Then you'd do well to keep your whiskey flasks from Jim," Evans said. "He's a worthless man when drunk. He's shot a man for half a cause, and even threatened me, in an ugly fit, and more than once."

Early on the appointed day, Jim arrived at Evans' cabin. With few words, the party set off. Jim wore deerhide pants held on only by a scarf worn as a belt, a leather shirt with three or four buttonless waistcoats over it, and a hat left over from Jim's service as an Army scout. His days guiding emigrants across the prairies had left another mark on his costume. Jim just didn't feel dressed without a knife in his belt, a revolver in his waistcoat pocket and a rifle balanced across his saddle.

They rode the first half mile at a hard gallop, then Jim reined his small Arab mare in beside Isabella. Rogers and Downer, ignorant of the way, ate dust behind.

"How many people live in Estes?" Isabella asked Jim.

"Only half a dozen, year-round," he replied. "And if the Earl of Dunraven has his way, there won't even be that many. He wants all of Estes Park as his private hunting preserve. He's been hiring bums off the streets of Denver to file claims on 160 acres each, then he buys them for a song. It's completely illegal. Dunraven's man Haig tried to get me to sell, but I ran him off my property with a shotgun. And Evans, the fool, is buddying up to Dunraven so Dunraven and his guests will stay at Evans' hotel. Game's already getting scarce. Soon there won't be enough for a man to live on!"

After five hours the party crested a ridge at 11,000 feet and caught their first close-up glimpse of Longs. Isabella gasped.

"It looks so grand! And so ghastly!"

"And you're going to climb it, Miss Bird," Jim said. Then they plunged back into the forest, where dead branches threatened to toss them from their horses and tore at the blankets strapped behind their saddles.

Toward evening they neared timberline. The winter gales seemed to have tortured even the living trees. Wind had sucked the dead trees chalk dry and burnished them to an ashen sheen. Isabella was glad to throw herself into making camp in the highest grove of silver spruce.

Jim soon had a fire crackling and strips of beef sizzling on pine skewers. After supper they sipped tea and sang Negro spirituals and hymns, then "The Star-Spangled Banner" and "The Red, White and Blue." Jim recited some of his poetry.

At 9 p.m. the thermometer showed 12 degrees of frost. They were glad to roll themselves in their blankets. Though tired, Isabella could not sleep. She lay awake till dawn, watching the moon ghost through the spruce, and listening. Wolves howled far off, and the wind moaned over the rocks high above.

They rose in the numbing chill before sunrise. Isabella was tending the teapot when Downer strode up.

The Narrows at 14,000 feet on Longs Peak terrified Isabella, but not half as much as the Homestretch just above.
Photo by Glenn Randall.

"Come quick," he said. "Jim says he's never seen such a sunrise."

Isabella joined Jim where he was saddling Isabella's horse. The sky flushed pink, then rose. In an instant, the plains shed their gray for purple. "I believe there is a God!" Jim said.

"Yes, Jim, yes," Isabella murmured. "I have known Him for a long time." They watched without words for a long time.

"Jim, let us make a pact. Whoever dies first will appear to the other as a spirit, to prove that our beliefs are correct."

"Agreed," Jim said.

By 7 a.m. they were on the move. Isabella rode until the boulders grew too rough for her horse; then she joined the others on foot. They leaped from boulder to boulder, breathless in the frosty air. Jim panted to Isabella, "I was thinking in the night about your traveling alone. Where do you carry your derringer? I can see no sign of it."

"But I have no pistol."

"What? You should buy one at once!"

She stopped for a moment and laughed.

"For your sake, Jim, I'll carry one."

At midmorning they reached the Keyhole, a sharp notch on Longs' north ridge. Direct ascent of the ridge was impossible. They began to traverse a shelf called the Ledge toward a gully, the Trough, which would lead them to the west ridge and then the summit. Jim, in the lead, rounded a horn of rock and stopped abruptly. A smooth tongue of icy snow, 100 feet across and steep as a church spire, blocked access to the Trough. Isabella shrank against the rock.

"Let me go back to the Keyhole and wait for you there," she begged Jim.

"We'll just descend below the snow and reach the Trough lower down," he said.

"Nonsense!" Rogers said. "Let her go back. Without her, we can go straight across. A woman is just a hindrance up here."

"If Miss Bird does not go on, neither do I," Jim replied.

"Come on, Downer," Rogers said. "We can kick steps up here." The pair disappeared.

For two hours Jim and Isabella lowered themselves from boulder to boulder. Isabella grew giddy with fatigue and altitude. Her arms ached. She would have retreated only halfway down had not Jim helped her with every step.

At last they rounded the base of the ice tongue and began climbing the Trough. Isabella's thighs throbbed. Stones rolled beneath her feet and battered her shins. Jim kept saying, "There's no danger, Miss Bird. Only a short bad bit ahead. You'll go up if I have to carry you!"

Just below the west ridge Isabella used Jim's shoulders to surmount a giant boulder and discovered Rogers and Downer waiting on top.

"Let's go," Rogers said, dragging her over the crest. "We must keep moving. We've been waiting here for hours." Isabella was too winded and thirsty to reply.

Here at timberline in Jim's Grove, with Mt. Meeker in the background, Rocky Mountain Jim wooed Isabella Bird.
Photo by Glenn Randall.

They continued across a second narrow ledge with a fearful drop-off to their right. At the ledge's end they reached the final 500-foot slope. The pink granite appeared nearly perpendicular. Beneath them the slope swept unbroken to Black Lake. "One slip," Isabella said to Jim, "and a breathing, thinking, human being will lie 3,000 feet below, a shapeless, bloody heap!" Downer began to look a little ill.

Isabella began the Homestretch. She walked, then staggered, then crawled, alternately pushed from below and hoisted from above. Every six steps she stopped to suck great gulps of air into her parched lungs. Her mouth felt like she was chewing cotton. Rogers soaked a snowball in Jamaican ginger from his flask, hoping to revive her. Her thirst only worsened.

She could think of nothing but the next foothold. Her eyes stayed fastened to the rock beneath her. Suddenly she realized that the stones bruising her knees were level. The summit! She closed her eyes and waited for the world to quit spinning. Then she looked about her.

North and south, to the horizon, peaks rose 11,000 and 12,000 feet above the sea. To the east the gray-green plains rolled out for 150 miles.

"Jim, it's so quiet. So peaceful. Thank you, thank you, ever so much." Jim only nodded. His eyes sought hers, but her eyes were roaming the distant ranges.

They could not remain long. Downer was coughing blood and looked about done in. Jim went first on the descent. Isabella supported her feet on his shoulders. At the west ridge they parted again. Rogers and Downer took the direct but steep way back to the Keyhole. Isabella and Jim retraced their path of the morning. Isabella kept slipping on bits of ice and crashing into boulders. Again and again Jim made steps for her of his hands and knees, or pulled her over steep sections with his lariat.

At 6 p.m. they stood again at the Keyhole. Isabella was thirsty beyond measure. Three times Jim thought he spied water amidst the boulders and discovered only ice. A fourth pocket yielded a mouthful, but it only dampened Isabella's throat. Jim carried her the last 100 yards to her horse and lifted her gently to the saddle. He held her upright as they made their way slowly back to timberline. At camp he wrapped her in blankets and carried her to her bed of spruce boughs. She fell asleep in minutes.

Rogers and Downer had preceded them. Now they made a great show of being eager to start at once for Evans'. Jim said quietly, "Now, gentlemen, I want a good night's rest, and we shan't stir from here tonight." The young men unpacked, their grumbles intended for Jim's ears. Downer immediately collapsed into his blankets.

When Isabella awoke several hours later, Rogers and Downer had already eaten and crawled off to sleep. Jim sat with the fire's glow playing over the handsome side of his face. Moonlight bathed the spruce, and only the fire's pop and hiss broke the silence of a windless night. Isabella propped herself up on a roll of blankets near the fire. For some minutes neither said a word. Then Jim spoke.

Nine months after Isabella left Estes Park forever, Griff Evans, Estes' first hotelkeeper, shot Rocky Mountain Jim. In this picture, taken years later, the murder seems to haunt him still.

Photo courtesy the Colorado Historical Society.

"If you want to know how nearly a man can become a devil, I'll tell you now.

"I was the son of an Irish officer quartered at Montreal. I fell in love, at only 17, with a girl as beautiful as an angel. My mother disapproved. She thought I was too young. I took to drink to spite her. Then I ran away from home." A tear moistened his eye.

"I joined the Hudson's Bay Company as a trapper. War broke out, and I signed up with the Union Army. I stayed with them when the fighting was done, as a scout. Then some buddies and I found out there was more money in banks and stagecoaches. We'd knock one off and go on a real binge, get into fights. I left more than one cowboy lying on a barroom floor. I don't know if all of them pulled through or not. Some of them looked awfully still.

"Then I came to Estes, five years ago, in 1868. I was going to try to live quietly, but I like the whiskey too much. I'm afraid my sprees in Denver have marked me here as well."

"Give it up!" Isabella cried. "Give up the whiskey! There is still time!"

"I cannot," he said. "It binds me hand and foot. I cannot give up the only pleasure I have."

Isabella felt tears come to her own eyes. She reached out and caressed his hair. He seized her hand.

"Isabella, will you — could you — stay with me?" She sat stunned, her thoughts churning. Could it possibly work? She hesitated a moment longer. Then, slowly, she pulled her hand from his grasp.

"Jim, it cannot be. Even if every circumstance were favorable, and I could love you with all my heart, I could not trust my happiness to you. You've lived a desperado's life too long. Don't be angry, Jim, please. It cannot be."

Jim bowed his head. Unnoticed, the fire had begun to die. They sat in silence a moment longer. Then Isabella rose and limped back to her bed.

They reached Evans' cabin at noon. Isabella continued her journey several weeks later. Nine months passed. On September 7, 1874, an apparition startled Isabella in her Swiss hotel room, its 16 golden curls still dripping blood from the wounds torn by Griffith Evans' shotgun shells. Rocky Mountain Jim made his final bow and vanished. Isabella learned later that the ghost had appeared at the exact instant of Jim's death. She said only, "Jim was a man whom any woman could love, but whom no sane woman would marry."

Enos Mills inspects the coming season's cone crop.
Photo courtesy the Denver Public Library, Western History
Department.

WIND

Winds only annoy — or so most people think. They steal your hat and ruffle your skirt, blow hair into your eyes and frost through your bones. But mountain winds play rougher. One winter's day on Longs Peak, the wind carried off Enos Mills' hat — and nearly took him with it.

As always, Enos' curiosity started the adventure. Strange winter winds, warm and boisterous, had often shaken his cabin walls. He had watched them devour snow-banks like a plague of locusts, leaving behind only muddy meadows. Up high he had seen them smear a recent snowfall in banners across the sky. Just how hard were those winds blowing? He ordered an anemometer, the best he could find. The catalog proclaimed the meter's ability to record winds of 170 miles per hour. "That's *more* than enough," Enos exclaimed.

When the meter arrived on a crisp autumn day he took it to Granite Pass, five miles west and three thousand feet above his cabin. There, at 12,000 feet, a thousand feet above timberline on the northeast shoulder of Longs, he anchored the meter to a boulder half as tall as a man. The breeze registered a gentle — for Granite Pass — 25 miles per hour.

That winter, whenever the wind promised a record, Enos returned to Granite Pass. Often he felt like a man who had overindulged on New Year's Eve. He would lean into the gale blowing out of the west, battling for every yard, then collapse on his face when the wind dropped to nothing. Always the wind drove harder as he neared the pass. Once the gale forced him to crawl the last dozen yards. He took shelter behind the boulder to which the instrument was tied. Then he raised his head, blinked, and looked again. The dial read 120 miles per hour. He crawled away from the pass until the wind eased a little below the crest. Then he stood up and skipped down the mountain with the wind at his back lengthening every stride into a giant's.

February brought a snowstorm followed by clearing and cold. Enos noticed one afternoon that the temperature at his cabin had risen a few degrees. He went to bed early, wondering what weather the next day would bring.

Had Enos owned a barometer, he would have noticed a sudden drop in air pressure accompanying the climbing mercury. A friend west of the Divide would have noticed the same, but his barometer would have registered less than half the change. A warm air mass 200 miles across had entered Colorado. The mountains forced the air mass upward to regions of lower density. Then, like lead weights falling in a pail of water, the dense, warm air accelerated out of the less-dense regions and down the eastern slopes. The difference in pressure across the Divide thrust the wind forward faster and faster still as the air flowed from high pressure to low.

Toward midnight Enos cast back his blankets and sat up sweating. The fire he had kindled in his stove had burned low, but the cabin seemed hot. Had the place caught fire? Quickly he stepped to the door. The warm wind on his face soothed his fears. "Must be a chinook," he said. His thermometer read 35 degrees, almost a heat wave for the wintertime Rockies. He slipped back beneath his blankets, eager for dawn.

Enos awoke to the sound of a tempest combing the heights. The sound grew, died away, and returned, stronger than ever, a deep rumbling moan as a million trees scraped and bowed before the irresistable force. Enos tossed on his clothes and hurried out the door, neglecting even a handful of raisins for lunch. "That meter must be spinning like a fly-wheel gone crazy," he chuckled to himself. "Got to get up there and see what it reads before it blows away."

A hundred ascents had made the trail familiar. Enos paused to watch the tall pines sway in unison. "What's it like up there?" he wondered. "What's it like to dance with a tree in a windstorm?" He hurried on, for now he had a plan that required the tallest tree he could find.

At a grove of Englemann spruce he turned aside. Spruce weren't noted for strength, he knew, but that only gave the plan zest. Selecting the tallest spruce in view, Enos shed his coat and shinnied up the branchless trunk like a bear. He climbed with ease; but then, he had figured once that he had been climbing trees for 40 of his 45 years.

He did not rest until he sat, panting, upon the highest limb that would support him. One hundred feet above the ground, the tree-top bent as if made of rubber. The crown nodded east, then north and south, then cut a circle in the air the diameter of a waterwheel. Enos whooped and laughed. "I haven't had such fun since the circus came to town!" he yelled to the wind.

A sudden gust snapped the pattern. With a screech of splintering wood the entire grove tilted east. A tottering giant 30 feet away lost the ancient battle and crashed to the ground, dirt flying as the roots burst from the soil. A half-dozen saplings collapsed in its wake. Enos put three holes in his jeans and took off a square foot of skin in his hurtling descent.

Near timberline he chose a smaller, stouter tree, twisted but undefeated by a hundred storms. The tree vibrated like a gong under the hammering of the wind. Enos clambered to its top. Several times the gale nearly ripped his hands from the limbs. Gusts spat gravel at him the size of peas. He winced when they found bare skin. From his perch he watched in awe as the wind scraped a yellow plume off Granite Pass. "Hoo, boy, it's going to get *nasty* up there!" he said. "Let's go!"

The tree-dwarfs at timberline provided a little shelter from flying sand. Enos stepped out of their protection and promptly flew over backwards as a gust punched him in the chest. After rubbing his bruises for a minute, he made his next attack at a crouching run. The blizzard of gravel nearly flayed the skin from his cheeks. He flung himself, gasping, behind a boulder. Shielding his face with slouch hat and mittens, he began to crawl. His coat drummed on his back as the air waves beat upon him. Once he sat up to survey the scene and was immediately blown flat. After that he took his bearings only behind a boulder.

Enos Mills first climbed Longs Peak at 16. He takes a rest here, at far right, on the Homestretch, just below the summit. Photo courtesy the Denver Public Library, Western History Department.

No birds flew, but he met a flock of ptarmigan sheltered by a snowdrift. A few nibbled on grass and seeds skating down the snow. Most huddled into hollows scooped into the drift. Now and then a savage gust tumbled a ptarmigan out of its nest. Without spreading their wings they would struggle back to their hollows. The ptarmigan took no notice as Enos crawled by within three feet.

Two hours later, Enos neared the pass. His clothes gaped at knee and elbow. As he crested the last rise he caught sight of the anemometer, its cups blurred with speed. The gusts almost lifted him from the ground. When they blew he could only shut his eyes and hug the earth. He could not face into the hurricane. If he turned his back the wind created a partial vacuum around his mouth and made him fight for every lungful. He could draw a deep breath only with his head turned sideways.

At the pass he huddled behind a boulder and watched the meter's needle. A gust struck and the needle bounded to 100 miles per hour. Seconds later came another. The needle hit 130. Then a thundering like an avalanche started. The mounting roar drowned every thought. Enos swore he felt the boulder sheltering him tremble. For an instant the needle shuddered at 170 miles per hour. Then something snapped with a report like a rifle-shot. The needle plunged to zero.

In a moment the gust subsided. Enos looked toward the summit. Snow-streamers level with the mountain-top painted the sky smoky white. "Must be blowing like a banshee up there," Enos whispered. "I wonder . . ."

In the next lull Enos took off uphill like a sprinter from the blocks. Whenever the surging currents threatened to topple him he threw himself behind an outcrop. Once above the pass the wind backed off slightly. He made good progress through the broad valley of the Boulderfield. At noon he neared the Keyhole, a narrow pass facing west into the teeth of the tempest. Air flooded the notch like a waterfall. Enos tested his strength against it and quickly decided to use a lower but broader pass where the wind had less force. Once on the west side the hurricane pressed Enos into the slope as he traversed a series of ledges toward the Trough, a gully leading to a razorbacked ridge with an abyss on the far side. In the Trough his troubles truly began.

At first the wind lent a wanted boost. Broad air masses sweeping up Glacier Gorge converged on the fan-shaped slopes below the Trough and funneled all their energy upward. Enos scampered up with an ease he had never experienced. But as he neared the top the wind took command. Whenever he stood up the wind shoved him prone again. He took to crawling. When he heard a big gust coming he hooked his feet beneath stones and sought handholds to anchor himself, limpet-like, to the slope. Then the worst gusts began to pry him loose from his holds. They lifted him an inch or two before slamming him back again. Progress came in yards, then in feet.

Shrieking hell broke loose 30 feet below the crest. Even "lulls" blew with typhoon force. "If a really big gust comes just as I get to the top," Enos thought, "it'll blow me right over the ridge top and out into space on the far side. I might not stop till I hit Wild Basin!"

Enos clung to the gully floor, pondering his next move. Another gust seized his body and shook him up and down like a rag doll. His feet began to come unhooked. If they slipped, he would cartwheel up and over the brink. Every muscle went rigid, then began to tremble. His fingers failed just as the gust relented.

The thought of being flipped end for end sparked a new strategy. Moving inch by inch, he turned around until his head pointed downhill. Now his feet could brace more effectively. His hands found better holds. He began to creep up the gully backwards, almost effortlessly as the wind did all the work. A grin cracked his battered lips. "This is the most ridiculous way to climb a mountain I've *ever* tried," he said aloud. The wind snatched the words past his ears without a sound.

At the top of the Trough he escaped onto a narrow ledge. Sheltered from the wind, he took a long rest. The summit lay only a few hundred feet above. When he had recovered some strength he scrambled along the ledge to the Homestretch, the smooth slabs leading steeply to the summit. The wind increased again as he left the lee of the rock wall. When he reached the slabs he hesitated. Ice sheathed the rock. Only a few knobs of granite protruded. The wind rolled steadily upslope. Enos realized he could skate across the ice sheet to the easier slope beyond — if the wind held. Cliffs below threatened if it faltered. He waited, testing the wind. Then he committed himself, feet dancing from knob to knob. Smack in the middle one boot missed its mark. His mittened fingers clawed the ice. The skidding boot scraped another knob, hung there momentarily, and broke loose again. His balance gone, Enos started falling sideways and got a glimpse of cliff edge below. Then the wind buoyed him. He lunged for a rock spike, caught it and hugged it tight. An easy scramble — for Enos — put him on top.

The wind booming up the mountainside shot straight up into space, leaving Enos on the summit in relative calm. He bounded over to the western edge of the summit plateau, eager to see what havoc the wind was wreaking at its source. Just as he peered over the edge a mighty gust bowled him over backwards. The string anchoring his tattered hat parted at last. His hat took off for Kansas like Dorothy for the Land of Oz. Enos laughed and waved farewell. The hat, a veteran of a dozen years of adventure, vanished to the east. "You thought it would be me, didn't you, wind. It just could have been."

Enos Mills snowshoeing in the Rockies.
Photo courtesy the Denver Public Library, Western History
Department.

BLIND ON THE CONTINENTAL DIVIDE

All night snow thickened the air. Every spruce limb bowed; every timberline rock lay smothered. An hour before dawn the snowfall ceased. Curled up in a battered canvas raincoat, a solitary figure slept between an overhanging boulder and a dying fire. Enos Mills awoke as the chill penetrated his clothes. Yawning, he cast another pine branch into the fire ring, blew life into the coals and dropped off to sleep again.

At the first glimmer of light, long before the sun peeped over the Continental Divide to the east, Enos awoke again. He stretched luxuriously. He was exactly where he wanted to be: in the mountains, unencumbered with tent, sleeping bag or cookware, and free to ramble and observe. He lashed on his snowshoes, slipped his hatchet into his belt and set off for timberline. He ate no breakfast, nor did he feel the need of it, which was good, for he had none in his pockets. He had eaten his last handful of raisins the night before. He planned to be home on the other side of the Divide that night, and he had often fasted longer than that. Once he had made three trips from his hotel, the Longs Peak Inn, to Estes Park, a distance of eight miles each way, then climbed Longs Peak by moonlight, all within 60 hours and all without food or sleep.

Enos could easily have avoided the treeless heights and hurried home to the endless chores of his crusade for national parks. But, as always, sunlight glinting off the high peaks seemed to call him. He went.

Within an hour the air had warmed. Sunlight kissed the snowy spruce tops. Enos paused beneath one to admire the blue and yellow sparkles. Without warning, the slippery limbs shed their load squarely into Enos' upturned face. In trying to dodge, one snowshoe trapped the other and sent him sprawling. He laughed and struggled to his feet, using his six-foot staff laid horizontally for support in the bottomless drifts. He dusted himself off, squinting, and realized the falling snow had swept away his snow glasses. He searched for a few minutes and gave up. "Don't spend too long above timberline," he reminded himself and continued upwards.

Above timberline not a rock showed. Every snow crystal seemed a dazzling, miniature sun. Eyes narrowed to slits, he snowshoed on. He wanted to see what creatures might be about and how the wind had tossed the snow into cornices.

For a while a herd of bighorn watched him curiously. Later he almost stumbled upon a flock of ptarmigan sitting motionless in the snow. For half an hour he photographed them with his battered Kodak. He noticed then that a grain of sand seemed to have become lodged beneath his eyelids. He plucked at them until the tears flowed, but the gritty feeling persisted.

At noon Enos reached 12,000 feet, the crest of the Divide. The diamond-hard glare had become a dagger to his eyes. He closed them, seeking relief, but the sunlight even stabbed through his eyelids. Forest shade would help, he knew. He quickened his pace.

Soon the pain forced him to stop every 100 yards and cover his eyes for a few seconds. Each time reopening them became more difficult. The periods of vision grew shorter and shorter. Finally he sat down and covered his eyes with his palms for a long minute. His eyelids seemed sticky when he rose to go on. Gingerly he tugged at the closed lids. The pain made him wince. He tugged again, harder, and almost cried out. His eyelids had become glued to his swollen eyeballs. "I'm blind," he whispered to himself. "Blind, on the Continental Divide!"

He groped for the staff standing upright beside him. Its solidity reassured him. Cabins, he knew, lay not too many miles to the east, and a trail to them began at timberline. But to the west lay only miles and miles of uninhabited country. Should he become confused and descent to timberline on the western side of the Divide, he might wander forever.

He could remember clearly the slope down which he must travel from his last glimpse before blindness. Feeling his way with his staff, he started downward. The hours ebbed away. "Where is timberline?" he said aloud. "I should have been there in half the time." He couldn't shake the feeling that he might be traveling west.

At each step he swung his staff left, then right, then planted it to steady himself. Surely, somewhere he would strike a tree! Hours later, or so it seemed, something snagged his snowshoe. He bent over to free himself and discovered a wiry evergreen hooked through the laces. Timberline! But east or west? He struggled on. When the trees had grown beyond the reach of his staff stretched upward, he began searching their trunks below snowline by feel. He had explored this part of the Rockies for 30 years, ever since he had arrived from Kansas as a farm boy of 15. The rise and fall of the land, as best he could judge, seemed familiar. He found only bark at the first tree, and the next. Then, at the tenth, his mittened hand struck a smooth place. He yanked off the mitten and examined the flat, recessed area with his fingers. No doubt remained. He had found a trail blaze.

Jubilant, he strode forward in the direction he thought the trail should go and felt the trunk of another tree. Another blaze! Without hesitation he went on, sinking his staff into the snow before him at each step. Suddenly he almost toppled onto his face. His staff had plunged into empty air. He probed right and left and discovered he had nearly wandered off a cliff higher than his staff was long. "I don't remember any cliffs east of the Divide at this point," he said to himself. Had he traveled west after all? The suspicion flooded over him. Certainly he was lost now as well as blind. "All I can do is find a stream and follow it downhill until I meet someone," he said.

A chill stole through the air as the sun slipped behind the ridge. In the shadowed forest Enos knew of the approaching night only through the drop in temperature. He backtracked a few feet and found a way around the cliff. Every few paces he shouted, then listened for a reply. None came; but he noticed that the echoes could tell him something of the terrain ahead. He seemed to be descending into a deepening canyon. It struck him that he

The Longs Peak Inn was both Enos Mills' livelihood and a means of teaching the value of wilderness.
Photo courtesy of the Denver Public Library, Western History Department.

might learn the direction the canyon ran by examining the trees on either slope. He knew that limber pines in that area grew primarily on south-facing slopes; Englemann spruce preferred northern exposures. If he was traveling east, there should be spruce to his right and limber pine to his left. He climbed up the canyon's right wall a few hundred feet and began examining the trees. The large, thin scales of bark peeled easily. "At least it can't be limber pine," he said, "and it might be spruce."

Quickly he descended the slope to check the trees on the far side. On the smaller, younger trees the bark felt smooth and resisted peeling. "Limber pine!" he exclaimed. "I've got to be east of the Divide, and I've got to be traveling east!" He set off down the slope with long strides, thrusting his staff ahead of him.

Before long the canyon narrowed. A windstorm some years before had woven downed trees into interlocking barricades. Large boulders choked the canyon bottom as well. Enos found himself first crawling, then walking a tight-rope. "Perhaps I can walk above this mess," he said. He climbed out of the canyon a few hundred feet and began traversing the slope. Unknown to him, the canyon wall grew still rougher. A cliff began to drop away on his left. Another began to rise on his right. The ledge between narrowed. His swinging staff struck the cliff on his right. He stepped left — and plunged through the cornice overhanging the cliff edge. For an instant he scrabbled frantically for a hold. Then he was falling.

Moments later icy powder buried him. A ledge 10 feet below the first had caught him. The drifted snow had cushioned his fall like a feather mattress. "Close," he thought. "Very close."

He began to explore his new ledge one small step at a time. Both ends dropped off immediately to depths greater than his staff could reach. He probed the outer edge — too steep to climb down. The wall above him rebuffed every attempt to find a hold. On impulse he swung his staff out horizontally. His staff thumped on dead, brittle wood. Reaching out to probe further, a dead branch almost poked him in the eye. He broke a piece off and dropped it, listening. He dropped another, and a third. "Can't be more than 30 feet," he said. He hesitated, trying to think of everything that might go wrong. Then he relocated the dead tree's trunk and leaned out over the abyss. Letting his staff go, he wrapped both arms and legs around the trunk and slid to the ground. He recovered his staff and set off again.

The echoes answering Enos' shouts told him the canyon was widening. Traveling became easier. An hour later he had just paused to shout and listen for a reply when a more ominous sound put every sense on alert. It began as a hiss, like the sound of a child's sled accelerating on snow, but no child was playing in those woods. Then the sound of splintering wood joined the growing roar, and the thunder of giant boulders colliding. Avalanche! Enos froze. Which way to run? The echoing canyon walls now told him nothing. Before he could decide, the wind born of the avalanche bowled him over. The din filled his brain. The ice-dust nearly smothered him. He tried to regain his feet, but a stray ice chunk whizzed through the air and exploded on a tree trunk nearby. Enos shrank back into the snow and shielded his head with both arms.

Slowly the rumbling ground to a halt. Heart still racing, stomach queasy, Enos stood up. He had taken only a dozen steps when he encountered the edge of the slide.

"At least avalanches don't strike twice in the same place," he said. He began picking his way over the hummocked wreckage. With a brittle snap the ice gave way beneath him. He twisted his staff to horizontal and stopped his fall, but his feet dangled three feet under the surface of the stream. He tried to push himself out with his staff, but his snowshoes became entangled in the ice. His thrashing brought down a crushing mass of snow. Silently he fought the weight trying to force him under. His numbed hands began to lose their strength. Then the stifling load slipped from his back. He floundered back onto solid snow, gasping for breath and shaking with cold. His clothes froze immediately in the sub-zero air. "Gotta build a fire," he mumbled through chattering teeth. "Soon as I get across the debris."

The avalanche had shattered trees into matchsticks and filled the canyon to a depth of 50 feet for 100 yards. Enos removed his snowshoes for better footing and carried them under his arm. As he began descending the far side his heels skidded out from under him. Like a bobsledder out of control, Enos bounced down the slope. One snowshoe slipped from beneath his arm and escaped his scrabbing fingers. Then the slove leveled out. Enos slid to a stop.

Immediately he felt about for the snowshoe. Without it he would be helpless in the deep snow. For an hour he searched in widening circles on hands and knees. Where could it be? He sat back on his haunches to rest. His feet felt like wooden blocks. Already, he guessed, the skin had begun to freeze. Within minutes, muscle and bone would follow. "I've got to have that shoe. Just got to . . ." His hand swept out again. It struck something soft. "What in the world?" Furry warmth met his groping hand. The avalanche had crushed a bighorn then spit the corpse back out onto the surface. With an effort, Enos hauled off his stiffened boots and shoved hands and feet under the carcass. Sensation came back in a painful rush. Lacing on his boots, he renewed his search. Still he found nothing. Then he remembered that last high bounce he took in his descent. "Of course, that's where it is!" he exclaimed. He began searching the broken trunks emerging from the snow. Perched just within reach, not 10 feet from where his slide had stopped, he found it.

He lashed his snowshoes on and headed down the canyon. At the first outcrop he encountered he stopped. The stream had soaked the black-tipped sulfur matches he carried in a tin box. Fortunately, his emergency supply in an oiled silk pouch had escaped wetting. Gathering wood with his hatchet, he built a fire and huddled down between it and the reflecting stone. Though the heat softened his icy clothes, it aggravated the pain in his eyes. He held snowballs to them, seeking relief, but the remedy did little good. The torment drove him away from the fire with his clothes still dripping.

Enos Mills in his "lobbying clothes" in New York. Enos led the fight for the creation of Rocky Mountain National Park. Photo courtesy the Colorado Historical Society.

He wandered on through the night, halting now and then to cool his fiery eyes with snow. At the first rays the renewed agony in his eyes told him of sunrise. "I've been traveling blind all night," he said. "I can't believe it." He inhaled deeply and signed. Then, puzzled, he inhaled deeply again. Some foreign odor was floating in the air. His nostrils sifted out pine needles, wet wool, greased leather, probing for the identity of the elusive scent. Wood smoke! Somewhere, perhaps still two or three miles off — the shifting breeze confused the direction — someone was burning aspen. He halloed mightily and listened. Only a sleepy chickadee answered. "Onward!" he cried, and pointed his snowshoes downhill.

For hours he trudged through the drifts. The smell of aspen grew stronger, but his shouts brought only echoes. By midafternoon his steps began to falter. Then his nose picked up a new scent: the mouldering reek of an old corral. He walked on, faster, till his swinging staff jarred to a halt. He reached out to the obstruction and let out a joyful whoop. "Anybody home?" he yelled. He began walking around the cabin, feeling for the door. "Anybody home?" he shouted again. Only the wind whistling through a loose rafter broke the silence. He found the door, the latch — and the board the homesteader had nailed across the doorway when he left for the winter.

Savagely he attacked the board with his hatchet. Ten minutes later the last nail gave way. He stepped inside. A fire was his first concern. Fortunately, the homesteader had left wood. Enos got a blaze roaring in the cast-iron stove and began steaming his eyes with snow dropped on top. After two hours the pain relented. The room grew warm. Enos leaned up against the wall near the stove and dropped off easily to sleep.

He awoke hours later to a frightening discovery. He could not move his legs. The fire had flickered out long ago. A penetrating chill had stolen into the room, numbing his still-damp legs and almost freezing his hands. Frantically he beat life back into his limbs. When his hands could hold a match, Enos rekindled the fire. For an hour the shivering racked him. Then life returned to his legs.

Hungry, he searched the cabin but found nothing, not even a can of beans. He turned to his pockets. Crammed deep into a corner and covered with lint, he discovered a dozen raisins, his first mouthful in 60 hours. Further searching proved fruitless. He rammed two more big logs into the stove and let sleep overcome him again.

Toward noon the raucous squawk of a Steller's jay jarred him awake. He stepped to the cabin door, and the jay landed on his shoulder. "Say, you're a friendly fellow," he said. "That homesteader must have fed you well. I'm sorry, but there's nothing to eat, not for you or me. You'll just have to wait till he comes back." The jay flew away complaining. Enos again caught the scent of aspen burning. "It can't be far now, can it, Mr. Jay?"

Once more he steamed his sightless eyes. Then he wrote a note explaining the shattered door and missing firewood and set off on the road that led down the valley through dense woods.

For a while he walked at almost a normal pace, listening to bird songs and reveling in the afternoon warmth. Then his staff and stumbling feet told him he had missed the road. He searched right and left and only bumped into trees. "Perhaps the road simply narrows for a while," he said. He went forward again, probing the snow with his staff. Air met his staff just as the surface started to give way. He leaped backwards to solid ground. "Some old prospector's hole, I bet," Enos said. He realized now where the road was. He had simply taken a dead-end fork. He backtracked 200 yards into the sunshine of the main road. "Slow down, Enos, you're almost there," he told himself. "Got to be almost there."

When the shadows of the roadside trees enveloped him he knew sunset was near. Abruptly the shadows vanished and the smell of wood-smoke grew strong. He had entered a clearing. He paused to listen, hoping for a human sound. Then, from within hand's reach, a little girl's voice broke the silence.

"Are you going to stay here tonight?"

Agnes Wolcott Vaille.
Photo courtesy the Colorado Historical Society.

TRAGEDY ON LONGS PEAK

Carl Blaurock's warning still rang in her ears as Agnes Vaille stared out at the bleak wastes surrounding the cabin at timberline. A few stunted trees poked out of the snow, their branches warped eastward by winter gales. For the moment, only fitful gusts rattled the roof of the cabin on Battle Mountain, the northeast shoulder of Longs Peak. Agnes knew that such comparative calm could not last. Winter, 1924, had started early with a series of vicious storms, and the first two weeks of the new year had given no sign of being different.

"I doubt we'll go today, Elinor," Agnes said. "The last time we tried the east face, in December, the sky looked like this and we had to turn back below Broadway. We didn't even get halfway."

The cabin door creaked open. A broad-shouldered man, 6 feet, 2 inches and 225 pounds, filled the doorway. Walter Kiener dropped his armload of wood next to the stove. Though the stove top glowed red, Walter's thermometer, hanging nearby, registered only 25 degrees. Elinor Eppich went outside for more wood.

"What do you think of the weather, Walter? It looks unsettled to me."
Agnes had seen a lot of Colorado weather. She had been rambling over
Colorado's Fourteeners for a dozen years, in winter and summer.

"Could go either way," Walter replied. "I think we should set out and
see what happens."

"Do you?" She paused, reflecting.

"I know how you feel," she said. "We've been up here four times now,
and I'd hate to make it five. We got so close when Carl was with us!
Another hour of daylight and we would have made it. We only had fifty feet
to go to the ridge, and from there it was easy."

Her tone changed abruptly.

"Carl's awfully worried about us. You know that, don't you, Walter? He
just flatly refused to try again. 'It's too dangerous, Agnes,' he told me.
'Wait till spring, when the weather is more stable. I won't go again and I
hope you don't either.'"

"We can take care of ourselves," Walter replied. "I've seen bad weather
in the Alps in winter, too, and a party of two moves faster than three."

Agnes considered for another minute. Then she nodded firmly. "All
right, let's do it then," she said. Immediately she began sorting her equipment.

The cabin door shuddered open again and Elinor struggled inside with
both arms full of wood. Snow swirled in with her, adding to the inch-thick
layer already covering the floor.

"This ought to keep us warm." She flung the wood onto the pile and
began digging through her pack. "We can brew up another cup of tea and
relax a little longer. I know none of us got much sleep, hiking half the night
and getting here at 3 a.m."

Elinor pulled the tea bags from her pack.

"Then we can start on down the trail and get a hot . . . . . Agnes, what are
you doing? I thought you weren't going to try it today!"

Agnes was inspecting the climbing rope foot by foot.

"We've decided to go take a look and see what the weather does. If it gets
no worse, I think we can do it. Walter says we'll only need about seven
hours to reach the top and no more than that to get down."

"But it's already 9 a.m.! Even if the weather holds, you'll still be back
long after dark. And how can you know how long it will take? Nobody's
ever done it in winter."

"We'll be all right," Walter said soothingly. The two climbers finished
packing.

"We'll see you tonight at the Longs Peak Inn." Agnes shut the door
behind them. "It'll probably be pretty late."

Agnes and Walter started upward, bracing now and then against a gust
that whipped snow against their knees. A hundred yards away they looked
back and waved. Elinor watched until they disappeared over a knoll.

"She really trusts Walter," Elinor thought. "I hope he's worth it."
Elinor started down the drifted-over trail to the Longs Peak Inn.

Two miles above timberline, Agnes stopped.

"Look, Walter, you can see the place where we turned back with Carl!" Agnes pointed at the tiny ledge marked by a smear of snow and hurried forward for a better view. The east face was just coming into sight around the shoulder of Mt. Lady Washington. Patches of light swept its dark cliffs as the sun played hide and seek with the clouds.

"Maybe we'll get good weather after all!" she exclaimed.

Walter smiled. Though a year younger than Agnes at 30, he played the role of guide. He had more experience, especially on snow and ice. Most of his experience had come in his native Switzerland. He had only moved to Colorado a year and a half ago. He had heard stories of winter winds that built to hurricane strength with astonishing speed, but he had never experienced one. He rather expected to find the stories exaggerated. Had he asked, Agnes could have told him the stories were true, but he did not ask.

"Let me break trail for a while, Agnes," he said. "You've been setting a merry pace since timberline. You don't want to wear yourself out down here."

"Oh, if you insist," she said. Walter noticed that she was breathing hard as he passed and took the lead, his massive thighs churning up and down like a pile-driver as he tramped out a trail.

At the base of the east face Walter uncoiled the rope and tied it to one end. With Agnes belaying, he began climbing, his movements relaxed, his progress slow but steady. Their route — the only one on the east face — was called Alexander's Chimney, named after Professor James Alexander, who had made the first ascent, in summer, three years before. Only half a dozen parties had succeeded in repeating the route. Even in summer the climb remained a prized accomplishment.

Soon Walter encountered ice. He unlimbered his ice ax and began chopping steps. Agnes, standing knee-deep in snow, felt the cold seep through her clothing. She wished she had stuffed newspapers inside her shirt for added insulation as Carl Blaurock did.

After 120 feet, Walter found a ledge and sat down in the snow. He stamped his big nailed boots in securely and began to belay. Agnes tied in to the other end of the rope and started up. Walter had not anchored himself to the rock, but the 100-pound difference in their weights made him confident he could catch any slip as long as he kept the rope taut.

Agnes joined him on the ledge, a bit warmer for the exertion. She anchored herself to a rock-spike with a bight of rope and belayed as Walter again took the lead.

Three more rope-lengths went by slowly. At 3 p.m. they reached Broadway, the sloping shelf almost halfway up.

"I think we're going to make it," Agnes cried. "The last 1,000 feet are supposed to be easier, aren't they?"

Walter nodded. In their excitement, neither noticed the thin, lenticular clouds forming to the north, a sure sign of high winds aloft. But they did notice the angle of the sun, and began to hurry.

Hard ice, deep drifts and snowy rocks frustrated their hope for speed. Fully 500 feet of elevation separated them from the summit when the sun touched the horizon. Walter, working hard in the lead, had eyes only for the slope ahead. But Agnes watched the sunlight ebb and noticed that the weather had begun to turn. The wind, gusty all afternoon, steadied and began to rise. The temperature dropped. Agnes clapped her hands and stamped her feet, but warmth no longer returned as it once had.

"Can you hurry, Walter?" she shouted. "I'm getting cold."

Walter looked down at the hooded figure half obscured by flying snow. He had not understood her words, but he guessed their meaning. At the next ledge he brought her up to join him.

"Chilly, don't you think?" she said when she arrived. Her numb jaw muscles made her smile rather crooked.

"It's 14 below." Walter tucked the thermometer back into its metal case. Agnes' smile faded.

"We've got to decide, Agnes: up or down? What do you want to do?"

Agnes hesitated.

"Darkness will catch us either way," Walter went on. "We're close now. There'll be a moon in a bit, and we've got flashlights."

Agnes looked down at the way they had come. Already the wind buried their footsteps. Chasm Lake 1,500 feet below appeared only dimly through the storm.

"It's a long ways down," she whispered. "Such a long, long ways down."

"What's that?" Walter asked.

"Let's go on, Walter. But please, let's hurry. I'm so cold."

Within minutes the last light ebbed. The hours crawled by uncounted. Kiener kept the lead, battling for every yard. It seemed the wind's banshee wail would never cease. Exposed skin could not endure the blast. Both climbers cowered when the gusts came, heads averted, eyes closed. The wind numbed Agnes' hands into clumsy claws. She could scarcely control her ice ax. Her feet had lost sensation hours before. She knew she might have frosted her feet and told herself she might lose some toenails, but deep down she knew she might well have frozen them far worse than that.

Twice in the storm they missed the easiest way and had to retreat from dead ends. Powder snow blanketed every hold. In the steep places, each hold had to be swept clear with a mittened hand. As often as not, the wind filled them up again before they could be used.

Agnes was forcing herself to think only of the next pitch when she staggered up to Walter's belay stance sometime in the blackest hours before dawn.

"Look above us," Walter said. Agnes thought she detected a smile splitting his lips. She looked ahead with wonder. Fifteen feet above them the slope leveled off.

"We did it, Agnes," Walter said. "I checked my watch. It's 4 a.m."

Agnes allowed herself to collapse into the snow.

"We should eat something here," Walter said. "It'll be windier on top."

"Yes, we should." She made no move to open her pack.

"Agnes, we've done it! We'll just go down the north face to the Boulder-field, and then it's only a couple of miles to the cabin."

He shrugged off his pack and dug out a bar of chocolate.

"Eat," he commanded. Agnes clutched the chocolate between the heels of her mittened hands and began tearing at the wrapper with her teeth. Walter swallowed a bar himself then dragged Agnes to her feet.

"Not far now," he said. "We'll just keep moving slow and steady — but we've got to keep moving."

Kiener knew Agnes would be safest going first down the north face so that he could immediately check any slip with the rope, but he dared not trust her to find the way. He started down in the lead. To the right, should he veer too far, lay a 2,000-foot drop-off to Mills Glacier; to the left, other cliffs could make descent impossible. Snow crystals imbedded in the screaming wind flayed his face like a cat o' nine tails. Never could he see more than a dozen paces ahead, and only then when his eyelids weren't frozen shut. Every few minutes he had to press his mittens to his face until the ice melted from the lashes.

Walter feared most the final 100 feet of the north face. There the broken ledges and boulder-filled gullies gave way to smooth slabs coated with ice even in summer and now undoubtedly plastered with snow as well.

At the top of the slabs Walter began searching for a place to anchor the rope for a rappel. He shouted to Agnes to wait until he found an anchor so he could belay her down the last tricky bit just above the slabs themselves. Engrossed in his search, he did not realize she had not heard until she was 10 feet away.

"Watch it! There's ice under that snow!"

His words came too late. Both of Agnes' feet skidded on the ice and she landed hard on her left side. She twisted face down and slammed her ice ax into the ice. Walter thought she'd stopped her fall, but her momentum ripped the ice ax from her frozen hands and she started accelerating again. Walter lunged toward her but he could not close the 10-foot gap between them in time.

For a frozen instant Walter watched as Agnes' inert body cartwheeled down the slab. Then he noticed the rope ripping out past his ankles. He tried to grab it but it was like trying to catch a snake's head in mid-strike. He flung himself backwards and braced himself for the inevitable jerk.

When it came the jerk scarcely budged him from his stance. He moved an inch toward the edge. The rope did not come tight again. He could just make out a crumpled figure lying in deep snow at the foot of the slabs. The snow had stopped her and prevented the rope from sending him flying after her, but he feared the bouncing fall had meant her death.

"Agnes!" he shouted. "Agnes!"

The only movement was the drifting snow already burying her body.

Elinor passed Sunday night at the Longs Peak Inn. She awoke at first light to the sound of a gale lashing the treetops. She rose and dressed quickly. In the main hall she encountered Herbert Sortland, a 20-year-old North Dakota youth who was winter caretaker of the Longs Peak Inn.

"Did Agnes Vaille and Walter Kiener come in late last night?" she asked.

"Haven't seen them," he replied.

Elinor stepped outside. Only a gray outline of the peak showed through the enormous plume of snow streaming out to the east.

"Maybe they're in the cabin," she thought. "But if not . . ." She realized that she could do little searching alone. Perhaps the men employed at the Inn to cut and store ice would come.

She went back inside and found Hugh Brown, his son Oscar and Jack Christian finishing breakfast. Without preamble she interrupted their conversation.

"Two friends of mine were climbing Longs Peak yesterday and didn't return. Will you help me look for them?"

"If Mrs. Mills will guarantee us a day's wages, sure," Hugh Brown said.

"Call her up then, right away!"

Christian went to call the owner of the Longs Peak Inn. In a few minutes he returned. "Let's go," he said.

Unnoticed, Sortland had entered the room.

"I'll come with you," he said. Elinor looked at the thin, sickly youth.

"I think we have enough people," she said gently.

"I insist," he said. Elinor shrugged.

Elinor lent them all the extra clothes she had. None of them, especially Sortland, seemed clothed to meet the blizzard above timberline. At 9:30 they set off.

Half a mile below the cabin the trees began to thin. The wind discovered them now and began to knock them off balance and fling snow in their faces. The cabin came into sight. Elinor looked eagerly for a sign of life, hoping her fears were childish and that Agnes and Walter were snuggled up to a roaring fire and would have coffee simmering and an exciting story to tell. . .

No smoke rose from the chimney. Elinor shoved the door open. The cabin was empty.

All five crowded inside. Many of the cabin's logs had come unchinked, and spindrift constantly sifted through the cracks. Christian kindled a fire while the others hauled in wood. Huddled about the stove, they discussed the next step. The snow stealing into the cabin landed on their shoulders and did not melt.

"We need more help to really look for them," Elinor said. "I'll go back down and call the Park. Will you go on and look for them?"

The four nodded. Elinor noticed that Sortland was shivering even as the fire singed his coat.

"I'll be back with more people and food as soon as I can."

Elinor buttoned her coat tight around her throat and headed into the blizzard again.

"Why don't you and I go scout the east face?" Christian asked Sortland. "You two can stay and keep the fire going."

"Agreed," Hugh Brown said.

The demon gale seemed bent on thwarting any progress. Time after time it stopped them dead in their tracks, or simply blew them over backwards. After an hour, Christian, in the lead, began to wonder how far they would get. Then he heard a muffled cry from behind him.

"Christian! I can't go on! My face is freezing!"

Christian staggered back to him. White patches covered Sortland's cheeks and the tip of his nose.

"Let's go back," Christian said. "This is madness."

"Any sign of them?" Oscar asked as the pair floundered through the cabin door, their ice-encrusted clothes crackling.

"We had to turn back below Chasm Lake." Chrisitan thrust his hands within an inch of the stove. "It's blowing about as hard as I've seen it blow."

He turned to warm his backside, then cocked his head toward the western window.

"Did you hear something?"

The sound came again, unmistakable this time in a lull in the gale.

"Help!"

All four bolted out the door. A tall, husky figure was struggling to regain his feet in a deep drift. He dragged himself upright, took one step and crashed into the ground again as an unexpected gust hit him like a battering ram. Christian reached him first and helped him to his feet. Walter could scarcely spit the words past his bluish lips.

"Agnes! She's alive! You've got to help me. She's lying beside a rock, up there." He flung an arm in the direction of the Boulderfield. "She can't live much longer. My God, what a storm!"

They helped him into the cabin. In a torrent of words he told them of the climb, the descent, Agnes' fall.

"I couldn't believe it when I got down to her and she spoke to me. 'I'm so tired,' she said. 'I must sleep, oh, sleep, only for half an hour.' I shook her. 'Agnes, we must go on. If we stay here we'll die.' 'Yes, I know I don't dare sleep,' she said. 'Oh, I hate to be such a nuisance!'"

Walter sucked deeply at the coffee they offered him. He winced as the searing liquid burned his throat.

"She roused herself then. I noticed she had lost her gloves. I pulled an extra pair of socks from my pack and handed them to her.

"You've got to help,' she said. 'My hands are frozen.' I looked at her fingers closely. They were solid white, dead white, all the way to the palms. She couldn't move them at all."

"I helped her pull the socks over her hands. Then I put my shoulder under her arm and we went on a little ways. Then she collapsed again. 'Walter,

I can't go on,' she said. 'My feet — I think my feet are frozen too.'"

Walter lifted his hands, palm upwards, and stared at them.

"I picked her up then. I picked her up and I carried her — oh, maybe a hundred yards. It was no use. I was so all gone and exhausted, I didn't have the strength."

He shook his head. "She knew it was no use, too. 'If we stay here we'll both die,' I told her. 'I'll go to the cabin for help and be right back.' She promised to wait for me. That must have been, oh, two hours ago."

Walter drained his mug.

"We must hurry!"

"Oscar, you keep that fire hot," Hugh ordered. Christian filled his thermos with coffee and the four men plunged into the tempest.

Within minutes Hugh realized his clothing could not begin to withstand the gale. "Christian!" he shouted, though Christian was only 10 feet away. "I'll freeze if I keep going. I'll go back and tend the fire and send Oscar down for more help."

He turned his back to the storm and started for the cabin with the wind driving him at a half-run.

"Let's rest a minute," Sortland said. His eyes shone bright and feverish from beneath his cap.

"We've got to keep moving," Christian replied. "If we don't we'll all freeze."

Just below Granite Pass, at an elevation of 11,700 feet, Sortland gave out completely. Christian and Walter divided his blankets and food between them, and Sortland started after Hugh, stumbling often.

"It's only a mile back to the cabin," Walter said, watching him go. "He shouldn't have any trouble."

Christian nodded slowly.

"He shouldn't."

For two hours they staggered, crawled, fell and picked themselves up again. Then Christian seized Walter's arm.

"Is that her?"

Savagely Walter tore the ice crystals from his eyelashes.

"She's moved! Maybe we're in time." Even as he said it, though, he had little hope for a second miracle.

Agnes lay face down on a boulder 50 feet from where Walter had left her. Her arms lay outstretched in front of her. Her pack, which Walter had left beneath her head, was strapped to her back. Walter knew before he turned her over what he would find. Her dead eyes seemed to stare into his own. He tried to close them, but the lids had already frozen.

"She must have been dead for several hours," he said to Christian. For the first time his shoulders sagged.

"Come," Christian said. "We can't do anything alone. We must get back to the cabin before we join her."

Christian pulled him away. Together, each supporting the other, they lurched down the broken talus. Walter fell often. Once Christian feared

The boulderfield on Longs Peak is a vast plain of granite at 12,700 feet. Agnes Vaille died near the left edge of the snowpatch.

Photo by Glenn Randall.

he would not rise again. But he pulled himself together and they went on.

Two hours after dark Christian threw open the cabin door. The shrieking gale seemed to fill the room as Christian dragged Walter through the doorway.

"Where's Agnes?" Hugh asked, looking behind them. Then, urgently, "And where's Sortland?"

"Sortland?" Christian was stunned. "Isn't he here?"

"I haven't seen him since I turned back."

"You haven't? He must be out there then. I hope he doesn't die like Agnes did!"

Sortland looked back once at Walter and Christian as he headed down from Granite Pass. Already they danced like a mirage in and out of the billowing ground blizzard. He shivered and hurried on, his shoulders hunched. The wind drove him like a scourge, faster and faster until he was almost running. His arms flailed about his head. He ran across a level terrace. Then he began leaping with gigantic strides down a steep moraine. A mighty gust flung him forward faster still. He thought he would land on his face. Too late he thrust a foot far out front, trying to slow down. His boot skated off a slippery boulder. With a sickening crunch his ankle twisted 90 degrees inward. He collapsed heavily on his right knee as pain seared the mangled joint.

When the agony subsided a fraction he tried to stand. The ankle buckled under a tenth of his weight. He tried to hop on one foot. The wind flattened him as if it were blowing over a straw. The realization of his predicament hit him like a sledge hammer. Christian's words came back in a rush. "Got to keep moving or we'll all die." He began to crawl, dragging the injured limb behind him.

While standing he could see which direction to go quite clearly. But on hands and knees he was essentially blind. The ground blizzard created a dense layer of flying snow three feet thick. Slowly, without knowing it, he veered from the correct course. By the time he reached timberline the boulders had shredded his pants and mittens. His exhausted muscles quivered and jerked convulsively. The snow deepened as he crawled farther into the trees. He stopped abruptly. He realized the wind would have filled his tracks hours ago, but the lay of the land looked unfamiliar.

"I'm lost," he whispered. The wind seemed to laugh insanely and the words echoed and re-echoed in his mind until they reached a maddening crescendo. "I'm lost!"

Snow packed into the holes in his mittens. For a while the warmth of his hands melted the snow. Then the soaking wool drained the heat from his fingers. The skin began to freeze. "I'll reach the Inn eventually," he told himself. "I've just got to keep moving."

On into the night he fought the pain and wind and cold, beating his way through the drifts for 100 feet, resting, then going on. The halts lengthened, the forward progress slowed. Once in the night he noticed that the trees seemed oddly missing for a few yards. He did not know that he had crossed the drifted-over road from the Inn to Estes Park. He fought for every yard, then every foot and every inch. A strange drowsiness seemed to be stealing over him. His ankle no longer hurt. He did not know that it had frozen solid.

"I'll just lie here a little while and take a nap," he murmured. His body seemed to be floating as he closed his eyes and let his infinite weariness wash over him.

Three hundred yards away a light suddenly shone out onto the snow. Oscar Brown hurried through the doorway of the Longs Peak Inn. Then the wind slammed the door shut behind him and darkness returned.

Bob Kamps (left) and Dave Rearick stand in front of their objective, the Diamond, at the Chasm Lake shelter cabin. Photo by Glenn Prosser, Estes Park Trail.

THE LURE OF THE DIAMOND

Trying to keep a mountain climber off a mountain is like forbidding candy to a child. The prize just becomes irresistible, especially when the prize is the Diamond, 20 vertical acres of granite brooding over Chasm Lake. The Diamond, on the east face of Longs Peak, soars from 13,000 to 14,000 feet. Stepping off Broadway, the severely sloping ledge dividing the Diamond from the lower-angled wall below, puts 800 feet of air beneath a climber's heels. Mountaineers shudder to think of the exposure at the top.

In 1954 Dale Johnson and Bob Sutton told the rangers at park headquarters that they planned to attempt the Diamond. The rangers immediately forbade it. Park Superintendent James Lloyd backed them up. The park could not have rescued them, and Lloyd feared the headlines any deaths would create.

Johnson returned to Boulder and organized his own rescue team. Lloyd didn't budge. For five years Johnson and others sought permission, without success. By 1959 the Diamond had become the most famous unclimbed wall in the country.

That summer Ray Northcutt and Layton Kor climbed straight up the most featureless section of the wall below the Diamond. Roger Contor, Wild Basin sub-district ranger, became convinced that if climbers could tackle the Diagonal, Northcutt's name for the new route, they should be allowed to try the Diamond. With the help of the Boulder-based Rocky Mountain Rescue Group, Contor felt the Park could pull a marooned climber off the wall.

That winter Contor persuaded Lloyd to allow a qualified team to attempt the climb. The team had to have two support parties capable of rescue. One group had to be on the mountain. The other had to be on call. The Park did not announce the new policy to the climbing community. They simply waited for the next never-say-die climber to knock on the door and find it, for the first time, open.

One day in late June 1960, a '57 T-Bird painted black and flamingo pink pulled up to the Longs Peak Ranger Station. Not exactly a car to escape notice; but that is precisely what Yvon Chouinard and Fred Beckey had in mind. They were set to steal Colorado's crown jewel, despite rumors of a year in jail and a $1,000 fine if they got caught. They did not know of Lloyd's change of heart. Their friends, Dave Rearick, a 27-year-old mathematician, and Bob Kamps, a 28-year-old schoolteacher, planned to help out if Yvon and Fred got into trouble. Bob's wife Bonnie made five.

Yvon and Fred hoped the climb would take only a day and a half, but they knew they still might be discovered on the wall. Chasm View, an overlook on the north face route, gives an unobstructed view of the Diamond. If discovered, rangers with handcuffs might well meet them on top. As a last resort they planned to abandon their gear and outrun the rangers down the south side of the mountain to Wild Basin and freedom.

They took a few days to scope out the route and soon discovered that John Clark, a ranger stationed at Longs Peak, was hiking up the mountain daily. Clark might easily spot them before they got off Broadway. The days stretched into weeks as Fred and Yvon pondered. In the meantime, Dave and Bob, climbers themselves with a dozen years experience between them, breezed up the second ascent of the Diagonal, the hardest route yet accomplished on the peak. Afterwards Bob and Bonnie hiked out for more supplies. Dave agreed to meet them the next day at the ranger station to help carry the food back in.

Bob ran into Clark in the parking lot.

"How did the Diagonal go?" Clark asked.

"It went well. That's a great route. We got a good look at the Diamond, too." He hesitated. "Would the Park consider an application to climb it?"

"Well, I can't give you permission. You'll have to go down to the Chief Ranger's Office and apply for a special permit."

"I'll do that," Bob said.

That afternoon Bob stopped off at the Chief Ranger's Office and asked that an application be sent to his post office box in Estes Park. Then he and Bonnie shopped and returned to the Longs Peak Ranger Station.

"Hey, Dave, how'd you like to join a Diamond team — legally?"

"I'd love it!"

The application arrived the next day, a Thursday. Dave and Bob filled it out, listing Jack Laughlin, a California friend traveling with them, as their primary support team, and the Sierra Club in California as the backup.

Twenty-four hours later the Park rejected their application. They wanted a stronger primary team and a more available backup. But the Park's reply didn't lock the door. Yvon and Fred realized they were about to lose any chance to be first, and left. Bob and Dave hustled down to Boulder to round up more convincing support. Immediately they ran into a roadblock.

The news that some Californians might get first crack at the Diamond outraged Boulder climbers. Rocky Mountain Rescue refused to help, saying they intended to back Johnson and Northcutt. Friends of Johnson tracked him down when he returned from a family camping trip and told him the Diamond might soon be opened. Immediately Johnson began organizing a team. Then Dave and Bob met Roy Holubar and their prospects brightened.

Roy, owner of Holubar Mountaineering, lent them a 1,200-foot rope so rescuers — they thought — could reach them easily anywhere on the wall. They did not know that the upper half of the wall overhung so much that any rescuers would be dangling in space, but the rope helped convince the Park.

Roy also introduced them to sympathetic Boulder climbers. Four of them agreed to join Laughlin as the primary support party. The Alpine Rescue Team of Evergreen promised to serve as a backup. Johnson, already days behind when he started, found out that Northcutt's job tied him down in Montana. On Monday Dave and Bob resubmitted their application.

Clark examined their equipment and told Contor they passed on that score. On Wednesday the reply came back from the Park.

"We are pleased to advise that final approval is granted for an attempted ascent of the Diamond during the month of August, 1960." The letter went on, "In the event of disaster, and after your party has exhausted its manpower and equipment resources, the National Park Service will be guided in its actions by the circumstances at the time."

They were on their own — but they were on their way.

A final flurry of preparation and the climbers, Bonnie and the support team started hiking in on Saturday. Between them they carried nearly 1,500 feet of rope, excluding the 1,200-foot single strand, which rode on a mule. Their packs jangled with 50 pitons, the hardened steel spikes to be hammered into cracks, dozens of carabiners, the aluminum rings with spring-loaded gates to clip rope to piton, and mounds of hammers, slings, rope stirrups and harnesses. The pack straps gouged their shoulders. As they neared the Chasm Lake shelter cabin they rested every 30 feet.

"I sure do hope no one else shows up here tonight, planning to do the Diamond," Bob said as they pushed open the door of the cabin. "We're first in line, anyhow."

An hour before sunset the cabin door creaked open. A middle-aged man stepped inside.

"Hi, I'm Glenn Prosser, editor of the Estes Park Trail. Are you the Diamond climbers?"

Dave and Bob smiled.

"We're going to try it, at any rate," Bob replied.

"Mind if I take a few pictures of you with the Diamond in the background?"

"Oh, I guess not."

Prosser snapped some photos, asked a few questions, and headed down in the fading light.

"I wonder how he got wind of this?" Bob asked. "We told the Park we didn't want any publicity." Dave shrugged.

"Beats me."

Sunday, July 31, dawned cloudy, with occasional dashes of rain. The permit said August, but they bent the rules a trifle and started humping loads up to the base of the route. To reach Broadway they planned to climb North Chimney, a rotten, ice-filled gully that splits the lower wall.

"Nothing like that in Yosemite," Bob said as they got their first look into North Chimney's clammy depths. Bob and Dave were rock gymnasts with little experience on big peaks. Mountaineer Laughlin chuckled. He tied in to the sharp end of the rope and began leading up the chimney.

"I'm glad you're along, Jack," Bob remarked at the top of the first lead. "I'm not sure we'd have got up this without you."

By late afternoon the climbers had fixed ropes up North Chimney to Broadway and carried the ropes and hardware for the climb to half-height.

"Still want to camp on Broadway tonight?" Dave asked Bob as they stood in the rain at the top of North Chimney.

"Not particularly."

"To the cabin," Dave said.

Monday broke windy but clear.

"Weather looks good." Dave stood in the doorway of the cabin. "Sure is cold, though."

Bob joined him. "Let's climb it."

The fixed line in North Chimney was as cold, wet and kinky as an octopus' tentacles. Bob and Dave took enough hardware from the cache to start the climb, while the support party trudged up behind them with the rest.

At 9:30 Dave tied in to one of their six ropes and started up the first pitch, a broken, rounded buttress. He ran out the 150-foot rope within minutes on the only easy climbing they would see below the summit.

Bob climbed "free" for a while on the second pitch using the flakes and cracks for holds. Then the first of two overhangs forced him to hang a three-rung rope ladder from a piton driven into a crack. With the ladder for hand and foot holds, Bob climbed as high as he could and still hang on to the carabiner clipped through the piton's eye. He drove another piton, climbed up the stirrup hung from it, and pounded in a third. Stretching out of the top rung, he reached a good hand hold and climbed free to a decent ledge.

As Dave finished the next pitch he felt a drop of water on his cheek. He looked up. Already charcoal clouds boiling over the top of the Diamond heralded the afternoon thunderstorm. But the water didn't come from them yet. Six hundred feet above him, the crack system they were following gaped into a chimney. A steady stream of water fell from its black depths. Dave wondered how hard the climbing would be in there. He noticed that the water fell free for 400 feet. At the Ramp, a sloping ledge 120 feet above him at the base of the overhanging headwall, the water was falling 20 feet out from the rock. "Pretty steep up there," he thought.

Dave's most immediate concern was the drops spattering the rock 100 feet above his head. The water turned 30 feet of the crack below into an oozing gutter. Bob joined Dave and led on, over a second roof and up a crack filled with well-watered grass. After 40 feet the rock became positively slimy as he reached the lower edge of the water-washed area. The clouds threatened to burst any minute. Bob anchored in a hurry.

"Let's get out of here!" he said when Dave came up to him.

Leaving ropes fixed up to their high point they sped down three rappels to the bivouac site their support team had built on Broadway. As quickly as they had come, the clouds broke up.

"We ought to be up there still," Bob said. Blue sky was appearing behind the thunderheads. "We've still got four hours of daylight."

"Too late now, I'm afraid."

"At least this way you get to lead the wettest part of that crack."

"Thanks a lot, Bob."

The Diamond starts at Broadway, the curving ledge halfway up the east face. In 1960 Dave Rearick and Bob Kamps climbed straight up the Diamond to the black crack leading to the notch in the summit. Photo by Glenn Randall.

Dave thought back to the water falling free.

"The water is hitting about 20 feet out from the base. Four hundred feet free and 20 feet out. It can't possibly be a 6 percent overhang, can it?"

Bob could not be dissuaded from the attack.

"Notice also, Dave, that the water won't be a problem after you lead through it. It doesn't touch the upper face the whole distance."

"But what about the upper chimney, Bob?"

"Estimating distance, Dave, it looks like you should have the honor."

"Thanks again, Bob."

Their support crew had brought sleeping bags up for the night on Broadway, a luxury they would not have should they spend a second night on the wall. Salami, raisins and candy provided dinner, and a lightning display over the plains the evening's entertainment.

The wall glowed orange in the sunrise as Dave and Bob used prusik slings to climb their ropes back to their high point. The prusiks, knotted around the fixed rope, held fast when weighted and slid freely when released. One prusik led to each foot. They then moved the prusiks alternately. Dave yodeled as they prusiked. The echoes delighted him.

"I may have to lead this thing," Dave remarked as he examined the dripping crack, "but you've got to sit here in the waterfall and belay." Already the volume of water had increased as the sun began to melt the ice choking the chimney far above. Bob grunted and pulled the hood of his cagoule over his head.

Two hours later Bob joined Dave on the Ramp.

"I'm glad to be out of that belay spot," Bob said.

Above them the wall overhung steadily for 400 feet. The rock, though dry, became crumbly. Their "crack" became a slot filled with loose blocks.

"Looks ugly, doesn't it?"

Dave nodded.

"I'll try to stretch the pitch out halfway to that ledge we spotted from Chasm View." Bob slung the rack of hardware over his shoulder. He winced at the weight. With a wad of nylon slings looped over the other shoulder and two ropes tied to his waist he waddled up to the crack and pounded in his first piton at arm's length.

An hour and a half later, Dave noticed a growing crowd of spectators at Chasm View. The crackle of a radio drifted through the still air. "Got to be the Park Service," Dave thought. Though nearly a quarter of a mile separated him from Chasm View, he could hear the spectators clearly.

"Is he halfway to that ledge yet?" Dave yelled to the crowd. "That ledge 200 feet above me?"

"Yes," shouted several voices.

"Off belay," Bob yelled down a few minutes later. "I'm going to put in a bolt to reinforce the anchors."

Bob got a hand-held masonry drill out of a bag clipped to his waist. Holding the bit against the rock with one hand, he began hammering on the handle with the other. At every blow he twisted the bit a quarter turn.

Twenty minutes later he pulled the bit from the hole, now 1½ inches deep, and hammered a soft steel stud into the hole. He clipped his rope into the bolt with a carabiner.

"On belay!" he yelled. Hand over hand, Bob hauled up the pack containing their bivouac gear and a little food and water. The pack did not touch rock once in 110 feet.

The next pitch went as slowly as the last. The sun left the wall, and Bob slipped into an extra sweater. He paid out rope by inches to Dave, hammering away above. Any chance of finishing the climb that day was gone. For a few minutes the sky grew black as the afternoon thunderstorm boomed overhead. The clouds spit a mouthful of hail, then a soft drizzle that slowly ebbed.

Suddenly the rope began to slip through Bob's hands by feet, then by yards. Dave had found a wide part of the crack that he could slip inside and climb free. Soon a merry "Off belay!" rang down from above.

"Good ledge," Dave called. "We can bivy here. It won't be too bad."

"Fantastic," Bob yelled back. The specter of a night spent dangling like a puppet vanished abruptly.

At 4 p.m. Bob set out to fix a rope as high as he could before dark. The wall overhung like the inside of a steeple, and the rock was more rotten than ever. Working hard, Bob made 80 feet before dusk. He anchored the rope to another bolt and retreated to the ledge, pounding out the pitons as he went.

On the ledge they pulled on their down jackets and cagoules. The waterfall, its source now only 150 feet above, occasionally sprinkled them. They divided their remaining food, saving only a few mouthfuls for breakfast.

A figure they could scarcely make out in the gloom appeared at Chasm View. Jack Laughlin's greeting echoed across the abyss. He had watched the pack hang free while it was hauled on the pitches below, and he knew the rock above was even steeper. A climber rappelling would be in the same position as the pack. After a 150-foot rappel, the climber would be dangling 10 feet out from the rock, unable to reach back in and place the next set of anchors.

"Will you guys be able to retreat after you prusik up tomorrow?" Laughlin yelled.

"We've been thinking about that," Bob shouted back. "Probably not. If that ice-filled chimney up there won't go we'll have to traverse off somehow, or have you come get us."

"Understood," Laughlin yelled. "Have a good night." He started down toward the cabin.

Darkness came quickly now. Lightning flickered over the plains, reflecting off the clouds.

"I hope that doesn't come any closer," Bob said. They sipped sparingly from their bottles. They had only brought two quarts each, and the dry, high-altitude air had given them a rasping thirst. The ledge, two feet wide and seven feet long, would not allow them to sleep lying down, so Dave sat

The day after their successful climb the Estes Park Chamber of Commerce feted Dave (left) and Bob and Bonnie Kamps at the Rooftop Rodeo parade.

Estes Park Trail photo, August 5, 1960.

cross-legged, back against the wall. Bob managed to slump over on his side. Both checked that the anchors were secure and the ropes tying them in were snugged up short. Then they drifted into fitful dozes.

In the morning Dave prusiked up the rope to Bob's high point and led on a few feet to a small niche. Bob studied the problem of following. The top end of the rope was now anchored to the left and out from the bivy ledge. When Dave had prusiked, the lower end had been anchored as well. Bob had no such luxury. When he stepped off the ledge he would swing like a pendulum dropped from the height of its arc.

Bob untied the anchors and took all the slack out of the rope that he could. Then he walked into space.

A collective gasp rang out from the spectators already assembled on Chasm View. Bob swung out over the base of the wall, 1,400 feet of air beneath his knotted stomach. For a minute he swept back and forth, spinning gently. Then the pendulum slowed, and he prusiked up to Dave's belay.

The waterfall chimney started just above. After 30 feet, Bob, in the lead, ran into the waterfall's source. Water from the melting ice dripped from mossy chockstones. The boulders wedged across the chimney stopped him cold.

Bob climbed out to the lip of the chimney and peeked around the corner to the right. No cracks marred the wall. If the left wall were equally flawless he would have to battle the waterfall itself. He turned around carefully in the chimney and peered out at the left wall. A thin fissure split the rock, climbable — perhaps. Bob traversed out and began to aid up it.

The rope running through the carabiners behind him made a series of 90-degree bends. Each new piton added to the friction Bob had to overcome to pull the rope through the carabiners. When the rope drag got so bad that he could scarcely move he pinned himself to the wall and belayed, standing in slings. Thunderclouds began to gather once again.

Just above Bob the angle eased to vertical. The rock improved. After 70 feet of aid climbing Dave managed to traverse back into the chimney. The ice that created the waterfall filled the inner recesses, but the chockstones were below him. At 1:15 Dave emerged from the chimney and anchored at the top of the Diamond.

Minutes later Bob joined him. Bonnie scampered down the gully at the top of the climb and threw her arms around Bob as a burst of hail clattered around them.

"I'm glad you're back," she said, and gave him a kiss. A news photographer snapped a picture and grinned. His editor would be happy.

"Congratulations, you guys," Laughlin said.

"Thanks," Bob replied. "It was a real good climb."

Dave and Bob scrambled up the last 200 feet of talus below the summit. An astonishing scene waited for them. Several reporters from Denver papers fired questions at them while photographers clicked away. One announced he wanted a story on them for *National Geographic.* On the fringes of the crowd John Clark radioed the news to park headquarters.

"Great climb, great climb," wheezed a portly gentleman as he elbowed his way into the throng. "I used to be a climber myself. Never used them pie-tons, though."

"Pea-tons," Bob corrected him gently. The man did not hear.

"You've made the front page of the *Rocky Mountain News* two days running," *News* photographer Mel Schieltz said, "and if you give me a smile you just might make it again tomorrow." The shutter snapped. "Thanks a lot."

"The cars are double-parked on Highway 7," he added, "and one guy is selling peeks through his telescope for a quarter." He sighed and lowered his camera.

"This has been a hell of an assignment. I haven't got more than four hours' sleep the last two nights."

Dave wrote in the summit register, "First ascent of the Diamond," and signed his name. "Let's do it again in 20 years," Bob said, signing below Dave.

"All right," Dave said, smiling.

As they headed down the north face they quickly outdistanced the mob. Down in the Boulderfield they met a reporter defeated by the altitude. He asked, "Where's the party that climbed the Diamond?" Bob jerked his thumb toward the summit.

"Back there." The reporter hurried on. Dave and Bob burst into laughter as soon as the reporter left earshot.

A mile farther on they met a distinguished-looking man in his '40s and a 13-year-old boy.

"I'm Blake Hiester," the man said, "and this is my son Richard. We climbed up here just to shake hands with you. That was a magnificent climb."

They chatted for a few minutes, then Blake surprised them by inviting them to a steak dinner and a night in his cabin in Estes. They accepted eagerly.

At the Longs Peak Ranger Station they found the phone ringing off the hook. Some of Bob's former students called to congratulate them. Another call came from the Los Angeles *Herald Examiner*. The Estes Park Chamber of Commerce asked them to star in the Rooftop Rodeo parade the next day and offered to put them up for the night afterwards.

"Only if you send some mules up the shelter cabin to pick up our stuff," Bob said jokingly. The Chamber of Commerce man didn't hesitate.

"Certainly," he replied.

The next call came from KOA-TV, inviting them to appear on a talk show in two days in Denver, with dinner and a night in the Continental Hotel thrown in as incentive. Bob and Dave laughed.

"Why not?" they said.

"You know," Bob confided to Dave as they drove into Estes Park with Blake, "This whole thing has gotten rather blown out of proportion. The climb just wasn't that hard. There are a lot of people who could have climbed it."

"I know what you mean," Dave replied. "But we sure couldn't afford this ourselves. May as well enjoy it while it lasts."

Three days later Dave, Bob and Bonnie checked out of the Continental Hotel and drove back to the Longs Peak Ranger Station. They retrieved their equipment that their support party and some mules had brought down. Then they unrolled their sleeping bags in the Longs Peak Campground and fired up a pot of glop.

Dave thought of their life the last three days and laughed.

"Quite the contrast, hey, Bob?"

"Quite the contrast."

This view of the Diamond from Chasm View has inspired many climbers. In 1975, Jim Logan and Wayne Goss made the first free ascent of the face without using nuts or pitons as handholds.   Photo by Glenn Randall.

OUT OF THE ROCKING CHAIR

Hot tea and cold feet: Wayne Goss could think of little else as the snow soaked into his tennis shoes 150 feet below the base of the Diamond. Above him, Jim Logan was leading the final icy pitch of North Chimney while Wayne belayed. Wayne's socks squelched when he wiggled his numb toes.

An experienced climber such as Wayne would use Adidas on snow only for a very good reason. He had one. Jim and Wayne hoped to be the first to climb the Diamond "free," without clinging to pitons driven into the cracks. For three years, Colorado's best had tried and failed. Success would require moving fast and light, so Wayne had hiked up in tennis shoes instead of boots. He had a battered pair of tight-fitting RDs in his pack for the Diamond itself, and the tennis shoes would be lighter to haul up the wall. To save more weight, they had left the stove behind, and with it any chance of a hot drink. Wayne and Jim, both pushing 30, both, by reputation, has-been climbers of the '60s, were out to set new standards once again in 1975. You'd have been a sucker to bet even money on success.

Before that July, every ascent of the Diamond had been in the style of the first ascent 15 years before. Climbers had hammered in a piton, hung a three-rung rope ladder from it, climbed up three feet, pounded in another. A new style had emerged in the late '60s and '70s, at first applied only to lowland crags. Climbers had discarded those comforting steel handholds and begun examining the rock for natural ones. In the new game, only flakes and cracks could be used as holds. Heavy pitons were replaced by lightweight "nuts," aluminum wedges jammed into cracks at constrictions. Nuts could be placed and removed without the mini-sledgehammer needed to drive steel pitons. The rope, running freely through a carabiner clipped into the nut, would stop a fall, but only if the nut held, and only after the rope came tight. A climber 10 feet above his protection would fall 20 feet before slamming to a halt.

In the early '70s Jim had served two years in the Army. Wayne, too, had dropped out of climbing for a while. They found relearning to climb slow and painful. Both climbed only sporadically in the years preceeding the Diamond. Then, in the spring of 1975, Wayne and Jim began climbing steadily again. They wanted to know whether they could match the new standards. Wayne believed he could climb anything that had ever been climbed: Jim was not so sure.

By July they were knocking off hard free routes in the foothills around Boulder like so many tenpins. The warm, welcoming rock of Vertigo, Guenese, and the Naked Edge was a far cry from the storm-wracked Diamond, but it was a good start.

Rumors started flying that some hot Californians were about to raid Colorado and snatch the first free ascent of the Diamond as they had snatched the first aid ascent in 1960. Jim and Wayne hiked in one July afternoon knowing other teams might be only days behind.

"On belay, Wayne," Jim called down from the top of North Chimney. Wayne flicked the anchor nuts loose and began to climb.

"Sounds like someone's got a stove going!" Wayne said as he joined Jim at his belay. "Maybe we can beg a cup of tea."

They coiled their ropes and began traversing Broadway, the broad, steeply sloping shelf running the width of the east face of Longs.

Rounding a buttress at the base of the Kamps-Rearick route, they came upon three women bivouacked at the base of the wall. A large, torpedo-shaped haul bag and masses of equipment lay strewn about, the unmistakable sign of the aid climber.

"How are you doing?" Wayne asked.

"All right," replied Stephanie Atwood and Laurie Manson. Molly Higgins, leaning against the rock in the back of the cavelike bivy site, muttered something grumpily.

Wayne and Jim ambled past them and chose a bivouac site about 50 feet farther along the ledge, just beneath a small overhang and perched on top of a large snowpatch. They shrugged off their packs and strolled back to chat with the women.

"What route are you up for?" Jim asked.

"D7," Laurie replied.

Jim glanced at Wayne. "That's what we had in mind, too," Wayne said. "We thought we'd try to free-climb it." He paused, surveying the gear heaped in confusion.

"I think we'll be moving faster than you will. Do you mind if we go first?"

All three women had noticed the small packs Jim and Wayne carried. Molly in particular had noticed how much they seemed to feel at home on Broadway. She had no doubt they would feel equally at home on the wall above.

"You can go ahead if you want to," Molly said.

Wayne and Jim looked relieved.

"Thanks a lot."

"Would you like a cup of tea?" Laurie asked.

"I'd love it," Wayne replied. "I'll make you a deal, Jim. You get water and I'll lead that sixth pitch up there, the one everybody's been failing on."

"Sounds fair," Jim replied.

Jim slithered down the snowbank with a casual belay from Wayne and filled a water bottle where the melting snow trickled off the edge of the snow bank. At Molly's request, he also retrieved the rope the women had fixed from their bivy site to the water supply.

"Do you believe in omens?" Molly asked Jim as he returned. "I was about to go get water before you arrived and Stephanie said, 'You don't need a belay for that, do you?' I said, 'Oh, let's put one on just in case.' I got out in the middle of the snow and fell off. If it hadn't been for the rope I'd have gone head first down Field's Chimney. Doesn't that seem like a bad omen to you?"

Wayne Goss at his Boulder home.
Photo by Glenn Randall.

"I guess I don't believe in omens," Jim replied. Molly eyed him and thought, "I'll bet you guys make your own omens."

With a steaming brew in his hand, Wayne's feet began to thaw. From his pack he brought out a double handful of nuts, a few oranges and a chunk of cheese — the sum total of Jim and Wayne's food — and offered it around. Stephanie took a look at the meager supply and said, "We've got lots of food, hamburgers and mashed potatoes and stuff. Would you like some?"

Wayne tucked the fruit and nuts back into his pack.

"Sounds better than this," he said. "Thank you very much."

After supper they chatted for a while longer. The air began to cool, and soon their sleeping bags seemed inviting.

The next morning Jim and Wayne awoke at first light. The air felt warm when Jim thrust his head out of his sleeping bag. He hoped they could climb fast with bare hands even before the sun rose. Thunderstorms had been besieging Longs every day, and they expected another that afternoon. They had no time for tea. They stuffed a handful of something tasteless in their mouths while checking their ropes and the knots in their slings. Then they stowed their sleeping bags on Broadway and started climbing before the women had finished packing their haul bag.

Yawning and sleepy, Jim stumbled up the easy first pitch. The cold rock quickly numbed his hands. At a small stance he thrust them deep into his pockets and endured the pain as the blood came rushing back. After Jim anchored, Wayne followed the pitch slowly. He had on his favorite RDs and a pair of raggedy tan corduroys, both veterans of every hard climb he had done that summer. The tightly laced shoes pinched his toes, but at least they were dry.

Movement got Wayne's blood flowing faster. He picked up the pace on the next pitch. The four ropelengths above, each increasingly difficult, had all been free-climbed before. Alternating the lead, Jim and Wayne polished them off in a hurry.

"I feel terrific, Logs. I can't believe this was supposed to be hard." Wayne wore a broad grin as he joined Jim on top of the fifth pitch. The face was just slipping into shadow as the sun made its 11 a.m. departure. A few somber clouds began scudding over the top of the Diamond. The east-facing wall prevented any view of their full extent.

Wayne scanned the headwall directly above and the cracks skirting it to the left. Both had defeated all comers.

"I don't think I can climb that without yo-yoing it. I don't want to get lowered on the rope a bunch of times to do the thing free, especially with that thunderstorm moving in. I think I'll take a look over to the right."

Wayne traversed right to a nearby route called the Black Dagger. A perfect 1½-inch crack split the wall above him, climbable but for the river flowing down inside from snow melting high above. Steep, smooth rock blocked further traversing. Wayne studied possibilities for a minute. Then he climbed down 10 feet and tried again.

"I can climb over onto Yellow Wall," he yelled to Jim, "and we can climb it! Looks like cake!''

Wayne spotted a good rest spot 25 feet away. He placed two solid nuts and launched himself upward, 10 feet, 15 feet, 20 feet above his protection. Any fall now would be a 40-footer, probably longer by the time the rope quit stretching. Unexpectedly, the climbing got hard. He swung into a layback: feet flat against the wall, body hanging out in space, fingers pulling ferociously outward on a flake to press the feet into the holdless rock. Another move, another, and Wayne's weakening fingers clamped onto a hold like a jug-handle. Panting in the thin air, he clambered onto the rest he had spotted from below.

One hundred twenty feet higher, out of strength and out of rope, Wayne set up a belay in a small, black hole. The veins bulged in his swollen forearms. Jim climbed the pitch so fast Wayne could not conceal his chagrin.

"Was it easy?" he asked.

"Don't know. No place to stop and see."

Now the first raindrops began to fall. The wind, trapped inside the giant bowl formed by the Diamond, grew gusty, buffeting them from all directions. A dash of hail salted the rock.

Fifteen feet above Wayne's belay Jim reached a narrow ledge. Cracks continued upward from either end. Jim took a look at the right-hand set.

"This will go," he thought, "but if I go up here we've got to climb the last three pitches of Yellow Wall. If I climb the cracks on the left we'll hit Table Ledge and we can just scramble along it and up to the top."

Even through the mists he could see that the final leads of Yellow Wall verged on overhanging. But he could not see the easy traverse that started 140 feet up the right-hand cracks and led to Table Ledge. He turned his attention to the left-hand crack system, two sinuous fissures three feet apart.

Wayne leaned out from his belay.

"Which way are you going to go?"

"Left."

"Looks hard. I'm glad it's your lead."

Jim wiggled the first joints of his fingers into the thin cracks. His fingers formed a dam. The water draining down the cracks began to seep toward his palms.

"Good luck, motha," Wayne said.

Not a foothold marred the wall. Lichen covered everything, and the rain had turned it into axle grease. Jim smeared one shoe-tip into each crack and started to climb. "His feet can't possibly hold," Wayne thought as Jim stretched for a good finger jam. Jim's fingers sunk into the slot and he kept going. "Stay on it," Wayne shouted.

At the top of the pitch Jim found another little cave. His belay would have confused a spider. Ropes, knots, nuts and slings criss-crossed each other in tangled disarray. The rain beat down steadily. The crack above looked like the Naked Edge, the difficult route near Boulder that Jim and Wayne had climbed two days before. They thought it easy then, when the rock was dry and they were more than a mile and a half lower in altitude.

Jim Logan at home in Boulder.
Photo by Glenn Randall.

Jim thought it might not seem so easy now.

"I'm impressed," Wayne panted when he arrived at Jim's stance. "I can't believe you led it like that, without hesitation. That thing took everything I had."

Wayne peered through the rain at the crack above.

"Looks bad, doesn't it?" He sorted out the gear and made a feeble effort. Ten feet off the ledge he stopped, hung there for an instant, and climbed back down.

"I'm beat," Wayne said. "Do you want to lead it?"

Jim shook his head.

"Well, if I'm going to lead, I'm going to have to rest." Wayne looked around a bit. Rain dripped off the hood of his cagoule.

"Sure you don't want to lead?"

"That's OK," Jim said. "Go ahead and rest. We've got time. This thunderstorm will clear out of here eventually."

Wayne squatted on his haunches and looked out at the mists floating up and down the face. Jim dug an orange and a chunk of cheese out of the pack and divided them. For a few minutes they ate in silence.

"This reminds me of my first bivy on the Diamond," Wayne said, chuckling. "I crouched on that little two-foot ledge on the Kamps-Rearick all night long."

"You know, we could bivy and wait till morning, when the rock is dry," Wayne went on.

"It would be a long, cold night," Jim replied.

"It wouldn't be that bad. We could rap down one pitch to that grassy ledge." Logan shivered.

"But I've got more meat on my bones than you do, Logs."

"Let's just try to get off today," Jim said. "If you can't free the next pitch, just aid it."

Half an hour later the rain slackened. The wind blowing up the face had even dried the rock slightly. Wayne stretched his cramped muscles as best he could on the tiny shelf.

"I think I'll look off to the left." He traversed 10 feet, examined a dihedral, and came back for a rest.

"Not today," he said. "There's another crack farther left. I'll try that one." Thirty feet from Jim he reached a three-inch crack dripping water.

"Looks like it ought to take us to Table Ledge!" Even through Wayne's fatigue a hint of elation crept through.

"Looks like a grunt, though. I can climb it, but I can't protect it." Their lack of large nuts meant any fall would be long and serious. Wayne pondered the crack for another moment. "Even if I can't climb it," he added silently. "Jim can for sure."

Wayne shoved his hands into the crack and bunched them into fists, jamming his cold and tender skin against the sharp granite crystals. He kicked his feet in as well and twisted them until they wedged. Moving one limb at a time, he began to climb. Twenty feet up he found a lousy placement for his largest nut. Then he spied a bolt some forgotten aid climber had placed 25 feet above. The bolt looked like safety and he headed for it.

The bolt was worthless, rusted and sticking out of the rock half an inch. Worse yet, the wall steepened just above. The crack became a left-facing corner. In the back of the corner, out of sight from the belay, grew a thick bank of moss. Wayne climbed 10 feet past the bolt and tried to scrape the moss away. He might as well have clawed a sponge soaked in ice water. Immediately his fingers lost all sensation.

"My hands will be useless by the time I get this clean," Wayne muttered. "I sure can't climb it the way it is." He leaned back and looked around the corner to the right. A few flakes and nubbins protruded from the river flowing down the rock. He studied them carefully and pulled himself back in to rest. Bending backward again, he tugged the sleeve of his turtleneck down with his teeth and gripped it between his fingers. Then, squinting through his rain-splashed glasses, he began to dry the tiny holds. He splashed gymnast's chalk over the holds from the bag he carried clipped to his belt. He dried them again with his sleeve.

"I might be able to climb the face out here," he yelled down to Jim 50 feet below. "Watch me."

Wayne inched out on to the face, feeling out every hold with wooden fingers. Then he reversed the moves and regained the corner for a rest. Again he tried, and again he came back.

"What a bummer if we fail so high," Jim thought, watching him. "If Wayne can't do it, I know I can't."

Wayne tested the holds a third time, and a fourth. He looked down at the bolt, memorizing what he would hit if he took the thirty-foot fall he feared. If the bolt failed, the fall would double.

"Let the rope run real loose," Wayne told Jim. "Here we go."

"Man, that's pretty," Jim thought. Wayne was poised on insignificant bumps. Only a twentieth of his shoe sole touched rock. Wayne's left foot started to slip. He had to move fast. He raised his left foot high and nestled the toe onto a tiny hold just beneath his left hand. In slow motion he rocked up onto the hold and stretched his left hand up, up, groping . . .

A piercing cry split the mists and echoed off the amphitheater walls.

"Got it!" Wayne yelled. "We did it!"

Thirty feet higher Wayne found anchors on Table Ledge. "On belay," he shouted.

Jim dismantled his spider web with fumbling fingers and traversed awkwardly to the crack, stiff after sitting motionless so long. At the bolt he paused to study the face. The rain had returned with a vengeance.

"No way I can do that free," he muttered. "No way."

Reluctantly he faced the main crack. He jammed his hands into the oozing moss, seeking the slimy rock beneath. With aching fingers he swung into a layback. For 10 feet he found holds buried in the mud. Then the holds ran out. He looked to his right. There, waiting for him as it had

Roger Briggs belays Jeff Achey on the second free ascent of D1, the route Bob Kamps and Dave Rearick pioneered in 1960, using aid.   Photo by Glenn Randall.

waited for Wayne, he spied a giant handhold, a hold so good he knew that even exhausted he could never fall after he reached it — if he could reach it. He leaned back farther, both hands still in the crack. With dread he realized he couldn't hang on with one hand while he reached with the other. He cocked his muscles for one last effort. Then he lunged.

His hand hit the flake squarely and his fingers clenched tight. His feet skated off the slippery wall, but he had a death grip on the flake now and nothing could pry his fingers loose. With a final effort he struggled up onto the hold. A few feet more and Jim joined Wayne on Table Ledge. The Diamond lay below them.

"You know it really feels good," Wayne said. Jim smiled.

"It does."

"How did you do that last bit?" Wayne asked. "That's the only place on the route where I thought I could fall leading."

"Oh, I took the easy way," Jim said. "Through the moss."

Wayne laughed. "Time to remove these painful RDs," he said. He slipped his shoes off and plunged his hand into the pack. Abruptly an expression of distaste crossed his face. From the depths of the pack he pulled two dank, dripping objects.

"They haven't dried a bit, have they?" He laughed again and began lacing his Adidas back on to his cold, aching feet.

Eric Aldrich examines the crux of the "Casual Route."
Nuts hang from the gearsling around his shoulder.

Photo by Glenn Randall.

ALONE ON THE CASUAL ROUTE

"It's the old man's route!" Duncan Ferguson said. He set down the boot sole he was gluing in Komito's boot shop in Estes Park. "The easiest free route on the Diamond. If a bunch of old farts like Chris and I can do it . . ." He laughed, eyes bright with vivid memories. Chris laughed with him.

Duncan's lean body belied his self-description. The "Casual Route," first climbed only two days before by Duncan and Chris Reveley, might well be casual for them, but that scarcely made it easy. Rock climbing on a wall as steep as the Diamond, at 14,000 feet, with hail and sleet likely any summer afternoon, would never be the same as climbing in the foothills.

"How long did it take?" Charlie Fowler asked. Charlie and Dan Stone had dropped in to Komito's to chat after climbing a difficult route on Chiefshead, just west of Longs.

"About 10 hours, road to road," Chris said. Charlie nodded, a bit impressed. He made a quick calculation. Three hours to hike in, three hours to hang out on top and hike out . . . four hours on the climb? Only four hours to do a first ascent on a wall considered the ultimate free-climbing challenge only three years before? The times were changing for sure.

"I'd been up there before," Duncan explained. "A couple of times. You know those big dihedrals on Grand Traverse? I figured they'd be free-climbable. But, you know, there's all that aid climbing down below. So Mike Covington and I tried to traverse into the dihedrals from D1. It was pretty hard, and then it started raining, so we rapped off. Well, then Ken Duncan and somebody tried it, kind of angling up left, up higher, to this ledge, and it was easier. But it started raining again, so they came down. And then Ken and I went up there. I talked him into trying it low. It was still desperate, and then it started storming again, so we rapped off."

"Pretty stormy summer," Charlie said.

"Yea, pretty wet. So, anyway, when Chris and I went back we went Ken's way and it was easy." Duncan laughed. "Real easy. Chris led it. After the traverse we went up the corners, to where Grand Traverse joins Yellow Wall for a pitch. Then we traversed off on Table Ledge."

"Was the traverse from D1 the hardest part?" Charlie asked.

Duncan shrugged. Chris said, "Probably the pitch on Yellow Wall."

Charlie nodded. He had done that pitch with Dan when they did Yellow Wall two weeks before.

"I'll have to go do it sometime this summer," Charlie said. "Sounds really good."

"You should," Duncan replied. Then he added, "You know, it'd be a really secure thing to solo."

Charlie's eyes widened a trifle. "That would be wild!" he thought, but he kept the thought to himself.

Duncan did not mean soloing the Diamond using some cumbersome self-belaying system. He meant climbing the Diamond unroped, with nothing between the climber and the glacier beneath but strong hands and a steady brain. Almost any climber but Charlie would have dismissed such a suggestion automatically. But Charlie was no stranger to unroped climbs. Some climbers in Boulder, his hometown, joked, with a serious edge, of madness and of placing bets on how long he would live. Perhaps 100 climbers in the country, including some who doubted his sanity, possessed Charlie's strength and skill. Of those, only 10 dared trust that skill as absolutely as Charlie did on days when things "seemed right." Charlie once said, "People climb with a rope because they have doubt in their minds that they can do the climb. If you eliminate the rope, you have to eliminate the doubt as well."

Just a year before, Charlie had awakened to a cloudy dawn in Yosemite Valley, California, and decided on the spur of the moment to abandon plans he had made to climb The Folly with a friend. "I don't want to climb The Folly," he thought. "I want to climb the DNB." Charlie had seen the route from El Capitan, directly across the Valley: the direct north buttress of Middle Cathedral Rock, a superb, 1,600-foot granite rib. For 800 feet few landmarks indicate the way. Thin cracks start, run upwards for 100 feet, and end abruptly. Finding the route is like threading a maze. Many climbers have climbed into blind alleys. For them, with a rope, retreat was easy. For Charlie, without one, retreat could be almost impossible.

The most difficult pitch of the DNB lay only 250 feet off the ground. When asked later whether he could have climbed back down the crux moves, Charlie laughed. "Maybe," he said. "If I had that kind of fear in me."

Above the crux, with retreat improbable, Charlie faced 1,350 feet of demanding climbing. Two hours later he emerged on top, exhausted, his spirits flying. Parties of two, climbing with a rope, had often been forced to spend the night. Three hours later Charlie left the Valley as a steady rain began to fall.

The summer after soloing the DNB, Charlie and Dan began climbing together almost every weekend in the Park. But Dan had other plans for the weekend following their meeting with Chris and Duncan. On Friday Charlie called the Park to find out how many climbers had signed out for the Diamond. Half a dozen teams had planned attempts, including one each on Grand Traverse and D1. "Better get there early," Charlie thought. Then he drove his red VW van out to a mammoth party in Eldorado Springs.

The party was just getting wild when Charlie climbed back into his van at 11 p.m. He had drunk a beer or two, but nothing like the quantity some at the party had consumed. Charlie could see them still, dancing, silhouetted against the giant bonfire, in tune with the beat as if the music were a puppeteer. The van's engine coughed and started. Soon the noise of the party faded as Charlie drove into the night. He had told no one of his plans.

His clock read 1 a.m. when he pulled up to the parking lot at the Longs Peak Ranger Station. The lot was half full. He set his alarm for 2 and crawled into the back of his van for a catnap.

The alarm's jangle snapped him awake an hour later. He located his headlamp in the dark and gathered the few things he would need. He stuffed a wool hat, a baggie of granola and two Tiger's Milk carob candy bars, his favorite, into the kangaroo pouch of his cagoule, then tied the cagoule around his waist. He took a harness and a few nuts in case he wanted to clip in somewhere to protect a move or tie his shoes. He tied together the laces of his EBs, his stubby, skin-tight climbing shoes, and clipped them into a sling carried over one shoulder. He slipped his camera into a pouch on his belt and was ready.

Fifty feet up the trail Charlie stopped to sign out at the trail register. He glanced over the entries ahead of his, mostly enthusiastic hikers bound already for the walk-up route. Then he made his entry. Number in Party: one. Destination: Diamond, D1 to Grand Traverse. Time Departed: 2 a.m. The last two columns were for later: Time Returned and Did You Complete Your Climb? "I can always come back if I don't feel good when I get up there," Charlie thought. He started up the trail at a steady pace.

Almost immediately he overtook a pair of hikers, then another. Soon he passed a third group, this one larger, resting on rocks beside the trail or perched on their overstuffed packs. Their flashlights flickered over the pines and shone into Charlie's eyes. His night vision vanished and he stumbled over an unseen stone. The voices of still more hikers filtered through the night, laughing, cursing when they stumbled, talking of everything from lunching at dawn to quantum mechanics.

Only the boundary between earth and stars marked the eastern horizon when Charlie arrived at Chasm Lake. To the west loomed the Diamond. He could tell by the outline of its bulk against the sky. "This'll be outrageous!" he thought.

The hiker's trail ended at Chasm Lake, but Charlie knew the way. Three generations of climbers had worn a faint path around the north side of the lake. The path climbed steeply, then dropped and climbed again as it wove through the giant boulders that had fallen from the cliffs of Mt. Lady Washington. In places the trail vanished, but Charlie always found it again.

Past the lake Charlie climbed toward the Diamond on moraines left by ancient glaciers. About 5 a.m. he reached Mills Glacier, shrunk now to a fraction of its former size and scarcely distinguishable from a snowfield. With his tennis shoes he scuffed steps in the snow and climbed to the base of North Chimney. Inside the chimney his headlamp caught moss, then rock, then cracks weeping water. He moved carefully, searching with his eyes for unstable blocks, thumping every hold with the heel of his hand, listening for the hollow crack of a loose flake slapping against the wall.

At the top of North Chimney he rested briefly for the first time since leaving the parking lot four hours before. In the half-light before dawn he could see clouds massing to the east and the faint outline of the ropes a pair of Yugoslavs had strung on the first two pitches of the Grand Traverse.

Charlie Fowler, who climbed the Diamond without a rope in July, 1978, the first time it had ever been climbed in that style. Photo by Glenn Randall.

"Better keep moving," he thought. Rain before noon was a distinct possibility.

He looked about Broadway for a few minutes for Chip Chace and Steve Levin, good climbers and close friends who had bivouacked on Broadway before attempting Yellow Wall. In the dark he did not notice the two figures still cocooned in their sleeping bags not a dozen paces from the start of his route.

Charlie squatted on a semi-level stone, slipped off his tennis shoes and jammed his feet into his EBs. He wiggled his toes until the bones of his feet found the hollows they had pressed into the shoes' uppers, then he laced the EBs down hard. He clipped the tennis shoes by their laces into his harness behind him. His headlamp still lit, he started scrambling up the steep but easy buttress at the base of D1, the route pioneered by Kamps and Rearick 15 years before.

One hundred and fifty feet off Broadway the wall steepened to vertical. The sunrise glow made his headlamp unnecessary. Charlie switched it off and put it in the kangaroo pouch of his cagoule. He could see Broadway in the increasing light. Nothing moved. Beyond, down North Chimney, lay Mills Glacier, now 1,000 feet below.

"Well, here goes," he thought. His throat felt tight. He leaned back and studied the way ahead. The route started hard. For 75 feet a single two-inch crack split the wall. No corners offered rest; no chimneys offered a place to hide from the exposure. Footholds existed, some of them two inches across, but they jutted out too little from the vertical wall to allow a complete rest. Charlie started up, testing every hold.

After 75 feet the angle eased back. Granite flakes dotted the face to Charlie's left, tempting him to try to traverse low. Always, though, he remembered Duncan's experience. He did not climb as if he might have to climb back down every move, but he tried to make absolutely sure he was on route before he went on.

He climbed higher, searching for the ledge, almost invisible from below, that Duncan had described. Unexpectedly, he found it. The ledge shot across the wall for 30 feet before fading into a series of flakes 30 feet from the corners.

At the end of the ledge Charlie began testing the flakes, pulling outward to see whether they flexed away from the wall or rapping them with his knuckles. He avoided the loose ones by difficult reaches and high steps. With a rope and a partner he might have taken a slight risk that a hold would break. But with a fall unthinkable, he dared not risk anything.

The traverse ended at a two-foot wide chimney. Charlie slipped inside gratefully. A winch couldn't have pulled him off now. He looked back across the traverse and down the crack, assessing the possibility of retreat. He shook his head and started up.

The dihedrals occasionally offered good resting places. With legs spread wide, one foot on each wall, Charlie could take the weight off his arms. He found good hand jams deep in the cracks, but the cold granite numbed his fingers and the chilled skin tore easily. He looked down at one rest and noticed that the Yugoslavs using aid on the Grand Traverse had not even reached the top of their fixed ropes.

At the Yellow Wall bivy ledge Charlie took a rest. The ledge, eight feet by four, lay 1,500 feet above Mills Glacier, 13,500 feet above the sea. The sun broke through the clouds, bathing the wall in an orange glow. "I feel like a tourist," Charlie thought, snapping a picture of the sunrise. A few flowers adorned the grassy ledge. Charlie photographed them as well. Then, peering over the edge as far as he dared, he looked for Chip and Steve. He shouted once, twice, but no greetings echoed back. He tucked his camera back into its pouch and faced the crux pitch.

Immediately the deep, wide cracks vanished. Fingertips only would slip inside. The footholds narrowed to pencil-width. Charlie smeared the toes of his EBs onto each hold with precision. Once, years ago, he would have reminded himself not to move his foot once he had placed it on a hold. Now the reminder was ingrained in his subconscious.

After 50 feet the climbing eased up as the route led into another chimney. But Charlie knew the reprieve was only temporary. The hardest part of the climb was still ahead, an awkward bulge with footholds too far to the right to be much use.

At the top of the chimney Charlie took a last good rest. He checked the long sling he had doubled and looped over his shoulder. If the bulge felt insecure, Charlie planned to clip one end of the runner into his harness, the other into a fixed piton someone had left in the bulge. He could reach down and unclip the sling when he reached the good handhold, the bucket, at the end of the crux. The piton would provide a backup, though without a hammer to test it, its exact strength remained a mystery.

Charlie started up the bulge using the sequence of holds that had worked two weeks previously. The moves felt shaky. He clipped into the piton with his runner without further thought.

The crack fit his hands like a glove, but his footholds lay well to the right. The bulge bent him backwards like a limbo dancer as he tried to force his weight in as close to the rock as possible. Fifteen hundred feet of air dragged at his heels. The hand jams ran out. The bucket at the top of the bulge lay just out of reach. By feel, without looking, Charlie checked that his feet still rested securely on their sloping holds. Then he slipped his right hand out of the crack and began to reach.

The rough crack ground skin off the back of his hand, but Charlie didn't notice. He saw only the next hold. He felt only the friction of skin and rubber on granite. Pulling slowly, he lifted his head, then his shoulders past the hand buried in the crack. The bucket tantalized him, still just out of reach. He pulled harder, biceps knotted. Left hand strained toward the level of his waist, reached it. The fingers of his right hand inched over the lip of the bucket and clamped down tight. Charlie's pent-up breath escaped explosively. Unclipping the sling, he let it dangle and heaved himself up onto the hold.

Only a few vertical feet and a long traverse to Table Ledge remained, both easy, full of holds. His mind concentrated still. He climbed the final 10-foot headwall with care, and stepped onto Table Ledge. The Diamond lay below. He had been climbing only an hour and a half.

Abruptly his concentration broke. For the first time he felt weary, a weariness mixed with a soaring exhilaration. Almost giddy, he lay down on the ledge for a few minutes. Then he clipped his runner into a nut and leaned over the edge, looking for Chip and Steve. He saw no sign of them. Above him, the clouds had thickened and begun to descend. "I'd better get out of here," he thought. "It's going to start chucking any minute."

His legs felt leaden scrambling up the final 200 feet of easy climbing. At Chasm View he stopped to gaze out at the wall, now shadowed by clouds.

"This is wild, man," he thought. "I just did the Diamond. That was easy."

From Chasm View he spotted Chip and Steve only halfway up the wall. They returned his wave and hastened on, eager to be off before the storm broke. Charlie selected a slightly overhanging rock and curled up beneath it in his cagoule. He munched a candy bar and soon fell asleep.

He awoke long enough to see Chip and Steve reach Table Ledge in a downpour. An hour later they joined him at Chasm View.

"How did you like Yellow Wall?" Charlie asked.

"Beautiful," Chip said.

"Except for the rain on the last two pitches," Steve added. They talked for a few minutes of little things as rain ran down the sleeves of their cagoules and dripped from the brims of their hoods. Then Steve pointed at the Diamond.

"Are those corners over there that new route you were telling me about, the Casual Route?"

Charlie nodded. A faint suspicion began to dawn in Steve's mind. He noticed Charlie's EBs lying on the ground, and the lack of a partner.

"Are you up here to climb it?" he asked.

Charlie smiled, a broad, triumphant smile.

"I just did."

Scott Johnston and Eric Aldrich (above) free-climbing the Casual Route.   Photo by Glenn Randall.

A LAST ADVENTURE

The low rumble started beneath Bill Baker's bed, accelerated, and ended with a thud that shook the house. "The garage door," he thought. "Glenn's getting up pretty early these days." He opened his eyes. Not a glimmer lit his window. "Must be time to get up, though. Wonder what time . . . 4:30! What the hell's he doing up this early?"

Down the hall, Mary Kay Brewster, another of my roomates, awoke at the garage door's clatter. She had heard me planning the night before, half in jest, half in earnest.

"Holy Moly!" she thought. "Glenn must be going for it after all."

I tossed a leg over the saddle of my bicycle, gave the pedals a few quick strokes, then locked my running shoes into my toe clips. "How are you feeling this morning, muscles? You're going to work today like you've never worked before."

I had spent the summer and early fall immersed in Longs Peak lore. August's sunshine had lingered into October, and I wanted one last Longs Peak adventure before the winter snows. It seemed fitting to match legs and lungs to the mountain from its true base; not the trailhead at the Longs Peak Ranger Station, but the plains stretched out flat from the foothills to the Mississippi. I wanted to travel, by bicycle, then by running, from Boulder at 5,200 feet to the summit of Longs 9,000 feet above.

I had warmed up for this ascent two weeks before by bicycling to Brainard Lake and running up Mt. Audubon, a peak 10 miles south of Longs. I'd enjoyed it immensely, despite the 40-degree gale I met above timberline in my gym shorts and sweatshirt. But the road to Audubon ran more direct than the road to Longs, without any ups and downs; the trail is four miles shorter each way, and the peak itself stands 1,000 feet lower. I feared that Longs would be simply an ordeal. I wondered if I could even finish. Whatever happened, though, the day would be an adventure, and that was reason enough to try.

Twenty-five miles out from Boulder the pines high on the walls of South St. Vrain Canyon catch the first light. Cold handlebars and colder air chill my fingers. I hope I have brought enough clothes this time. A small pack riding on the handlebars holds an extra shirt, three Chunky candy bars, two Bit O' Honeys and a baggie of raisins and nuts. The food can't really fuel a 9,000-foot day, but my stomach probably can't tolerate more. I know what will happen if I run out of blood sugar. It's happened before on burn-out runs. A giddy feeling creeps over my brain, and my knees start wobbling like a skeleton coming unhinged at the joints. My concentration ebbs. I pick my feet clear of the stones in the trail by a thinner and thinner margin. Then, inevitably, it happens. At just the wrong moment, my mind floats into the fog. A boulder, even a pebble, hooks my toe. My running rhythm shatters. I fling arms, legs, anything forward to restore the flow, but the exhausted limbs cannot respond in time to the brain's commands. I crash on my face, shredding my knees and raking my chest with gravel.

"Keep your mind on your feet when you're running today," I tell myself. Thirty miles out from Boulder I crest the last rise of South St. Vrain Canyon and drop down towards Allenspark. Something is wrong. The bicycle doesn't accelerate the way the grade tells me it should. Then I realize that a bicyclist's worst enemy has arrived: headwind. Just beyond Allenspark I can see a mile-long upgrade pointing straight west, straight into the wind. "Just what I need," I think, "a good pump before I even reach the trail." I rip into a Bit o' Honey with one hand and my teeth, hoping a little sugar will spark the pistons.

Shift down, shift down, out of the saddle and start to work. Head low, back arched, watch for broken glass, grind those pedals around. A gust hits, kills the cadence, and I weave like a drunk across the highway. The gust eases and I pick up the pace again, just a fraction, just enough to keep going straight. I can feel the pressure mounting in my thighs.

Then the hill ends and the road turns north. The valley rises gently to the ranger station now, and the wind is off my left shoulder. I keep the pace easy, my gears in low, and start to sing.

Gravel paves the mile-long side road to Longs, and I dismount. The 45 road miles are done, but 5,000 feet of gain remains. Just down the road, Enos Mills' cabin still stands. No highways paved this valley when he battled wind and snowblindness and had a thousand other adventures remembered now only by the pines and the granite.

I hide my bicycle in the woods just below the ranger station and gulp my last Chunky. The final Bit O' Honey comes with me. Enos spent days in the mountains with nothing but a handful of raisins. Two ounces of candy ought to get me up Longs. I trot up the last quarter-mile of road and turn onto the trail without pausing. I've got six miles and 3,600 of gain to the Boulderfield. Then the trail ends and the last 1,400 feet lie up unstable talus and icy slabs so steep the horizontal distance doesn't matter.

Almost immediately I know I've got trouble. A pulled muscle in my thigh, healed and forgotten weeks ago — so I thought — begins to twinge. "If it gets too bad, I'll just have to go home," I think. "What a shame to have this annoying me."

"Excuse me," I say. The young couple decked out in heavy mountaineering boots and large daypacks steps aside with a surprised "Hello!" as I flit by, Nikes landing soundlessly in the sand. The altitude hasn't got to me badly yet, but it will, I'm sure.

Just below Jim's Grove, three miles up the trail, I spot two rangers up ahead. I catch them slowly and recognize Chris Reveley, who holds the record for running Longs: 1:23 up, 2:05 round trip. I'll be lucky just to make the top in two hours.

"How far are you planning to run?" Chris' companion asks.

"The top, muscles willing," I say, trying to find enough breath to reply without gasping.

They laugh. "Have a good run."

The wind kicks up as I go through Jim's Grove, and I pull on another shirt. Rocky Mountain Jim wooed Isabella Bird here and gave the grove its name. "In 1873, let's see, 107 years ago . . ." My brain can hardly handle the numbers. "Keep your mind on your feet, Glenn."

The wind blows harder on the open slopes below Granite Pass. I can sense what it must have been like when Enos had to crawl up this bit to check his anemometer. A group of hikers sees me coming.

"Hurry, hurry," one of them calls, "it's only the first lap." My brain squeezes out a reply with the pace of molasses dripping.

"I've already run the first lap," I say. "I rode my bike up from Boulder."

"Oh," they say, and pause. "Do you do this often?"

"On occasion," I say, and pass on.

The trail ends at the Boulderfield. I ask a hiker the time. It's 10:15, I've been running an hour and forty-five minutes. Chris was on the summit half an hour ago on his record run.

"You don't really think much about how you feel," he told me afterwards. "You just think about moving fast."

I can't follow that, I'm afraid. My thigh is hurting bad. I can hardly lift my leg, and my worry increases that I'll trip and eat gravel. My knees are starting to ache. I lapse into a walk, or rather a jerky hop, skip and jump as I start across the trailless field of boulders toward the north face. The talus quickly steepens, and the boulders start rolling under my feet. Walter Kiener tried to carry Agnes Vaille down this garbage that January night in 1925. I can hardly keep myself upright, much less carry 130 pounds. I can see why he failed and left her to get help. I know why she died, too. In winter the winds lash this land like the devil's scythe. I chew another bite of Bit O'Honey and feel a tiny spurt of energy.

I glance out past Chasm View as I go by. Half the Diamond drops away below my feet. The other half rears up higher still. Elkanah Lamb skirted that precipice, then nearly plunged down that gully over there. I know several mountaineers who took the ride Elkanah avoided. One of them tripped coming down on a winter's night and tobogganed 250 feet before stopping himself with the pick of his ice-hammer. He broke no bones, but he said he felt as though he'd lost a boxing match to a gorilla.

I remember, too, the climbers who didn't skirt the Diamond: Dave Rearick and Bob Kamps, the first by any means, and Wayne Goss and Jim Logan, the first to free-climb the wall. A vision returns of my free ascent of the wall two years before. We were running from a hail storm just like Jim and Wayne.

The end of the talus snaps me back to the present. Ice streaks the slabs of the crux of the north face. Agnes fell down these slabs. I have no rope, no hardware. But I know where the holds are, if they aren't buried too deep.

The ice forces me out onto the slabs themselves, away from the cracks and corners that provide security. I pad upward like a leopard stalking prey, hoping exhaustion and altitude hasn't affected my balance. After 150 feet the slabs break back into ledges and talus and snow patches. My pace quickens.

Three hundred feet above me the granite meets sky. Is that the summit? Murphy's first law of mountaineering states, the summit is always two bumps behind the one you think it is. But I've been here before, and I know I'm not fooling myself. That's the summit, all right. I top the last rise and stumble across the level talus to the highest point. Old Man Gun dug his eagle trap up here somewhere, but I'm too tired to look. I don't dare sit down. My legs would never straighten again.

"You wouldn't happen to have any water to spare, would you?" The hiker digs into his pack and produces a bottle filled with Wylers, sweet, lemony, slipping down my raspy throat like honey. That sugar will hit the bloodstream like jet fuel, but maybe I can make it down to my bike before I crash.

"Man, that tastes good," I say, and take another swallow. "I started out from Boulder on my bicycle this morning at 4:30 and I'm a bit dry."

"That's quite the toodle," the hiker says. I grin and look out to the plains. Boulder lies out there, lost in the haze.

"It's a helluva mountain," I say. "One helluva mountain."

GLOSSARY

aid-climbing — the technique by which a climber supports his weight in short rope ladders hung from a variety of anchors he has placed in the rock.

anchor — a point of attachment between the climber and the rock. An anchor may be as simple as a loop of rope knotted over a rock spike or as elaborate as an array of nuts, bolts and pitons.

belay — the technique by which a climber anchored to the rock protects the climber in motion. One end of the rope is tied around the moving climber's waist. The rope runs down to the belaying climber, who passes it through his left hand and around his back to his right hand. The belayer feeds out or takes in rope as the climber moves. In the event of a fall, the belayer clamps down on the rope with his right hand. The friction generated as the rope passes around the belayer's body allows the belayer to stop the fall. The belayer shouts "on belay" when he is ready to mind the rope. The moving climber shouts "off belay" when he is secure.

bolt — a soft steel shaft between 1½ and 3 inches long driven into a hole drilled into the rock where no cracks exist and used as an anchor.

cagoule — a knee-length, waterproof rain coat, usually a pullover.

carabiner — an oval aluminum ring three inches long with a hinged and spring-loaded gate in one side, used to connect the climber to his anchors and the climber's equipment to himself.

chimney — a fissure in the rock wide enough to admit the climber's body.

chockstone — a rock ranging in size from a fist to a house that has fallen into a crack or chimney and become wedged at a constriction.

exposure — the climber's term for the amount of air beneath his heels. Exposure exhilarates the expert and terrifies the novice.

free-climbing — the technique in which the climber supports his weight only from the hand and foot holds naturally present in the rock. The rope is still used to stop a fall.

harness — the nylon webbing tied around the climber's waist that is the point of attachment for the rope.

ice axe — a snow- and ice-climbing tool with a two-foot shaft, used to cut steps, stop a fall on snow and provide a handhold on steep ice. The bottom end of the shaft has a spike. The head has an adze on one end and a curved pick on the other.

jam — a technique of free-climbing a crack by inserting the hands and feet and twisting or bunching them until they wedge against the crack walls.

layback — a free-climbing technique in which a climber pulls out on a flake, leans back and presses his feet flat against the rock. Moving one limb at a time, the climber can ascend sections of rock without horizontal footholds.

nut — a wedge-shaped aluminum block designed to be inserted into a wide part of a crack and slid down to a constriction, where it jams and serves as an anchor. A knotted loop of rope passes through the nut, allowing the climber to clip himself to it with a carabiner.

pitch — a section of rock between two belay points.

piton — a steel wedge hammered into a crack and used as an anchor.

protection — the system of anchors the lead climber places to stop him if he falls. The rope from the belayer runs freely through a carabiner clipped to each nut, piton or bolt to the climber's waist. If the climber falls the belayer clamps tight on the rope. The climber falls twice the distance he is above his last piece of protection. Then, the rope comes tight.

prusik — a loop of rope knotted around a fixed rope in such a way that the prusik will slide freely along the rope when unweighted and hold fast when weighted. The climber ties two around the rope and places one foot in each. By moving them up alternately the climber ascends the rope. A mechanical version called a *jumar* has replaced the prusik in modern climbing.

rappel — a technique of descending by sliding down a rope. The climber clips the rope through a system of carabiners arranged as a brake and attached to his harness.

RDs — tight-fitting, smooth-soled climbing shoes resembling a high-topped sneaker made of leather.

sling — a knotted loop of nylon webbing.

stirrup — a short rope ladder, usually with three rungs, used as a hand and foothold while aid climbing.

talus — a field of boulders ranging from several inches to several yards in diameter. A field of smaller stones is called *scree*.